'I'm not a ter...
sexually frustr...

'A... yet you claim...

'I don't need one—I... ...ly happy the way I am.'

'Are you?' Those eyes were holding her with their mesmerising gaze so that she couldn't look away. 'It seems such a terrible waste—a woman who responds to a man's touch the way you do, sleeping alone at night.'

Dear Reader

In February, we celebrate one of the most romantic times of the year—St Valentine's Day, when messages of true love are exchanged. At Mills & Boon we feel that our novels carry the Valentine spirit on throughout the year and we hope that readers agree. Dipping into the pages of our books will give you a taste of true romance every month...so chase away those winter blues and look forward to spring with Mills & Boon!

Till next month,

The Editor

Susanne McCarthy grew up in south London but she always wanted to live in the country, and shortly after her marriage she moved to Shropshire with her husband. They live in a house on a hill with lots of dogs and cats. She loves to travel—but she loves to come home. As well as her writing, she still enjoys her career as a teacher in adult education, though she only works part-time now.

Recent titles by the same author:

SATAN'S CONTRACT

MASTER OF DECEIT

BY

SUSANNE McCARTHY

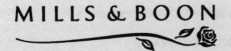

MILLS & BOON

MILLS & BOON LIMITED
ETON HOUSE, 18-24 PARADISE ROAD
RICHMOND, SURREY TW9 1SR

*First published in Great Britain 1993
by Mills & Boon Limited*

© Susanne McCarthy 1993

*Australian copyright 1993
Philippine copyright 1994
This edition 1994*

ISBN 0 263 78396 0

*Set in Times Roman 10½ on 12 pt.
01-9402-51109 C*

Made and printed in Great Britain

CHAPTER ONE

'WOULD somebody please explain to me what is going on?'

The voice that asked the question was very quiet and polite, but the smart-suited executives sharing the back of the sleek navy blue Rolls-Royce exchanged swift, anxious glances.

'I'm sorry, E.J. It seems to be some kind of demonstration. I'm sure it won't delay us more than a few minutes.'

Blue eyes, cold as newly sharpened steel, turned on the speaker. 'I can see that for myself,' the quiet voice stated. 'What I wish to know is why it is happening.'

The factory gates were blocked by a chanting crowd, some of them dressed as undertakers or skeletons. They were carrying placards, and a mock coffin. Someone, somehow, had got inside, and had climbed up on to the factory roof to erect a huge banner, a parody of the company logo. It read, "Preston's Poisons".

E.J. Preston glanced briefly out at the disturbance, and then back to his staff. 'Well?' One level dark eyebrow was lifted in cool interrogation.

'They're claiming that we're emitting toxins from one of our chimneys,' one brave soul admitted reluctantly.

'And are we?'

'There was a problem with the valves ...'

One glint from those chilling blue eyes warned that excuses would not be acceptable. 'Then see to it,' he instructed.

'Yes, of course. But you see, E.J., it's a problem with the production process. To change it could cost millions . . .'

'I said see to it.' The voice was still quiet, but gave clear notice that the matter was not open for discussion. 'I believe you know my views on putting profit ahead of environmental protection; however much money I may make, I am still obliged to live on this planet—I have no wish to hasten its destruction.'

Some of those listening took private leave to doubt that—there was something about E.J. Preston that was almost non-human. Maybe it was in the ice-cool precision of his mind, or the almost preternatural self-control that characterised all his actions. It was ten years since he had taken over control of the vast international business empire he had inherited from his father, and he was still only thirty-five. But anyone who had doubted his ability to step into the old man's shoes had quickly learned their mistake.

He was nothing like his father; Teddy Preston had been a plump and jovial character, courting publicity and beautiful women all his life. A self-made millionaire, he had lived life rumbustiously, defying his doctors with his fifty-year-old claret and his hand-rolled cigars, until the heart attack they had warned him of had claimed him at the comparatively early age of sixty-two.

No one would have dared called the son 'Teddy', although he had been named Edward for his father—

E.J. he had been since he had been a precociously
alert infant in his cradle. He had an aversion to publicity, and lived an almost ascetic lifestyle. In fact the
only thing he had in common with the old man was
a penchant for beautiful women. And they flocked to
him; not only was he extremely wealthy, but he was
unfairly good-looking too; hair as black as jet con-
trasted dramatically with those incredible blue eyes,
and his tall, lean frame was all hard muscle.

But it was something more than that which made
his attraction so fatal to the women who fell under
his spell. Maybe his air of cool, contained self-control
represented an irresistible challenge—each one wanted
to be the one who could melt through the icy exterior
to touch the heart that must surely lurk beneath.

The car had come to a stop again, blocked by a
particularly noisy group of demonstrators. The
chauffeur cast an anxious glance in his rear-view
mirror, encountering a level gaze from his employer,
and continued to inch forward, cleaving a path
towards the factory gates.

'Ah—here are the police.' The director of finance
sighed with relief as the sound of sirens split the air.
'They'll soon get this rabble cleared away.'

Some of the demonstrators wavered and fell back
as the police moved in, but the group in front of the
car stood their ground. E.J. watched, his eyes giving
nothing away as the scene unfolded. His only emotion
was a flicker of surprise at the realisation that the
figure in the midst of the group was a woman.

She was no beauty, that was sure, but she was certainly striking. She must have been almost six feet
tall, was angular rather than graceful, and the untidy

mass of curls that tumbled around her shoulders were of a shade that could only be described, even by the kindest judge, as carrot. But her eyes were alive with spirit, and there was a warning of considerable strength of character in that firm jaw.

Rather more character than was possessed by the young men around her, he reflected drily, watching as they held back, leaving her to lead the confrontation with the six burly police officers who were trying to move them on.

For a moment he toyed with the idea of intervening, but then changed his mind. Since she had evidently chosen martyrdom, instead of a more sensible way of approaching him with her case, who was he to deprive her of that satisfaction?

'Drive on,' he said to the chauffeur. The car eased cautiously around the blockade, and as it slid by he slanted one last look back over his shoulder. The girl was still arguing vociferously with the police. 'Women like that terrify me,' he murmured drily.

The other men in the car laughed in nervous relief at what was obviously a joke; there wasn't a woman born who could terrify E.J. Preston.

'Well, that wasn't exactly a brilliant success, was it?' remarked Andrea wryly, her fine grey eyes sparkling as she glanced around at the circle of faces gathered in the cluttered little bedsit which, as she was subwarden of one of the halls of residence, was hers.

'We got our point across,' Brian argued, considerably bolder now than he had been two hours ago in front of the factory gates. 'He saw our banner. We never intended to get arrested.'

'No. You all ran off like scalded rabbits as soon as the police appeared,' she reminded him with a touch of acid humour. 'And I don't suppose he took the slightest bit of notice of any of us.'

'So what are we going to do?' Roger asked, unpacking the tubs of curry and rice they had brought in with them from the Indian take-away. 'He's ignored us completely up to now—he didn't even respond to our petition. Whose is the chicken biriani?'

'Mine,' answered Brian, holding out his hand. 'Look, it seems to me that the time for petitions and letters to the papers is past—we need some real action.'

'Like what?' enquired Andrea drily.

'Well, we want him to read your report on the damage those emissions are causing, right? So, we kidnap him, and *make* him read it!'

'What?' She laughed in sheer amazement—even for one of Brian's wild schemes, this one was pretty outrageous. 'We can't do that! Quite apart from anything else, kidnapping's a crime.'

Brian looked a little affronted at her reaction. 'I don't mean *really* kidnap him,' he insisted. 'We just hold him for a couple of hours, long enough to force him to read the report. And we can get him to sign a document to say he's read it, and what he's going to do about it. And we can take photographs to send to the papers,' he added, warming enthusiastically to his subject. 'It'd be a fantastic publicity stunt—it'd probably make the front pages!'

'Our arrest would, you mean,' she scoffed.

'I'm prepared to take that risk,' Brian retorted, very much on his dignity. 'What about the rest of you?'

Roger looked a little uncertain. 'I don't know,' he murmured. 'I mean, how would we do it? I wouldn't want to have to hit him over the head, or anything like that—we might hurt him by mistake.'

Brian shook his head, sitting forward to urge his argument. 'We wouldn't have to hurt him,' he propounded earnestly. 'We could use fake guns...'

'No!' Andrea cut in sharply.

'All right,' he conceded, slanting her a look of irritation. 'I've got a better idea, anyway. Knock-out gas. I know someone who can get hold of a couple of canisters for us. No, they're not stolen,' he added, catching the glint of disapproval in Andrea's eyes. 'You can buy them perfectly legally on the Continent.'

'But you can't bring them into this country legally,' she pointed out.

'Well... No,' he admitted with reluctance. 'But what else do you suggest we do? We've been campaigning for months, and we've got absolutely nowhere. Do you want to just give up?'

'No,' she asserted forcefully. 'But I'm not prepared to get involved in anything that might turn out to be violent.'

'It won't be violent,' he insisted. 'I've got it all worked out. We've found out where he lives—all we have to do is wait outside one night until he comes home...'

'And then say, "Excuse me, Mr Preston, would you mind standing still while we spray this knock-out gas in your face?" Come off it. You probably wouldn't even get near him—I'll bet he's got half a dozen bodyguards.'

His face took on a sulky expression. 'OK—have you got a better idea?' he challenged petulantly.

'Not at the moment,' she confessed. 'But I'll think of one.'

He looked around to the others for support, but there was none forthcoming—they were all rather sheepishly intent on their food, evading his eyes. 'Well, let me know when you do,' he grumbled, rising to his feet. 'I'm going home.'

Andrea didn't argue with him, or try to persuade him to stay; in truth she was rather relieved that he had gone. Of course his idea had been quite ridiculous, but there was no accounting for the influence he might have been able to wield over some of the younger members of the group. Most of them were still undergraduate students, very bright and committed, but sometimes a little too impetuous. As a member of the university teaching staff, there was no denying that she had a certain responsibility towards them.

And besides, things had been getting a little... difficult with Brian of late. They had been colleagues and friends for several years now, but she was beginning to suspect that he attached rather more significance to their relationship than she did.

Maybe she had been guilty of misleading him a little she acknowledged wryly. Within the academic confines of university life the choice of eligible men was somewhat limited, and it was nice to have someone to go along with to the kind of formal occasions that she was sometimes expected to attend as a member of the faculty staff. She was going to have to make it very clear that she wished to keep things purely platonic.

Men had always been something of a problem feature in her life. As a teenager, she had always been terrified of being asked to dance at a party or a disco— the expression on the poor boy's face as she stood up, and he found that she towered over him, had been acutely embarrassing. And those that hadn't been put off by her height had been intimidated by her intelligence—biochemistry wasn't exactly a subject that people could relate to easily.

There had been one or two that could perhaps have been called boyfriends—at least there had been casually arranged meetings at pubs or parties, followed by a seemingly inevitable wrestle in the back of a car. But as soon as they had realised that her gratitude for their attention didn't extend to acceptance of their groping demands they had lost interest pretty quickly.

Only once had she given in. It wasn't that she had been any more in love with Alan, nor even that he had been all that much more persistent than the others. It had been out of a kind of weary desperation, to see if that would hold his interest a little longer. It had been a dismal failure, uncomfortable and embarrassing, and it hadn't even worked—it had been the usual, 'See you around.'

After that she had decided to devote her attention chiefly to her studies, and on the whole she was very happy with the choice she had made. She had gained her Ph.D. almost a year ago, and now had the chance to conduct research, as well as teaching at the university—which she enjoyed enormously.

It was just that sometimes . . . she felt a hollow little ache, deep inside. She would have called it loneliness, but that was ridiculous—she had a large family, with three married sisters and a clutch of nieces and nephews, and plenty of friends. And as sub-warden of a hall of residence that housed a hundred and twenty undergraduates, being alone was almost a luxury!

But glancing around at the eager young faces watching her with a touch of anxiety, she put on a bright smile, pushing her own slightly melancholy reflections aside. 'Cheer up!' she encouraged teasingly. 'We may have lost the round today, but we'll find a way to crack the bastard somehow!'

This really was millionaire's row, Andrea reflected with a touch of dry cynicism. The people who lived here could afford to cocoon themselves from the real world behind their thick thorn hedges and wrought-iron gates. The houses that loomed behind those barriers were large and imposing, the sort of houses that would have Jacuzzis and swimming-pools, and rooms stuffed full of priceless antiques.

And one of the most imposing lay behind the gates she was peering through. It must have had at least twenty rooms, to judge from the number of windows, not to mention a separate apartment over the triple garage—no doubt to accommodate the servants. A sweep of gravel drive lay between manicured lawns and immaculately kept rose-beds, all correctly pruned and ready for the coming of spring. There wasn't a weed in sight—she suspected that if one should dare to show itself it would be ordered off the premises as summarily as she had been.

Her blood was boiling. All right, so her old raincoat had seen better days, but that was no reason for that obnoxious butler—or whoever he was—to look down his nose at her as if she were some kind of down-and-out come begging at the door for a crust of bread.

Not that even a beggar would have deserved such an arrogant dismissal; but what else could she have expected? E.J. Preston had ignored her at every turn so far—she hadn't even got near him! She cast another disparaging glance up at the house. It didn't seem right that one person could have all that space to himself, while just a few miles away under the arches at Waterloo there were people sleeping in cardboard boxes.

And the fact that the money to pay for it had come from the destruction of the environment made her even more angry. Maybe Brian was right—he almost *deserved* to be kidnapped! Only something so drastic could make a man like that give any thought for other people's welfare.

Well, he needn't think she was going to just give up, she vowed resolutely. She was going to stay right here outside the gates—sooner or later he was going to have to come either in or out, and then she would catch him. And she would *make* him read her report— she would make it quite clear that she wasn't going anywhere until he did!

A glance at her watch told her that it was almost six o'clock. She had no idea how long she might have to wait—she had hoped to catch Mr Preston as he arrived home, but of course it was quite likely that a man like that would work till late. So long as he wasn't away somewhere on a business trip—she might end up waiting all night for nothing.

It might be a sensible idea to wait in her car; at least it would be a little warmer, even though the heater wasn't working. The elderly Beetle was parked at the kerb, and she cast a wry glance at it as she opened the door; it looked decidedly out of place in this elegant, tree-lined street. It was rather a mess inside as well—one of these days she was really going to have to get round to throwing out some of that rubbish on the back seat.

The radio could just pick up a programme through the crackle—the reception would certainly have been improved by a proper aerial instead of the wire clothes-hanger she had been using for the past eighteen months, since the last one had snapped off in the carwash. But that didn't really matter. Settling back in her seat, she fixed her eyes on that wrought-iron gate, and prepared to wait. And wait, and wait...

The hours ticked slowly away. It had rained for a while, and then stopped. A few people had passed, walking their dogs, and returned, gazing at the car with covert curiosity—they probably thought she was a burglar casing the area, she reflected with a twist of wry humour. *A Book at Bedtime* had finished, and she was listening to *Today in Parliament* when the lights of an approaching car caught her attention. It was a sleek dark blue Rolls-Royce; it was him!

Snatching up the report, she scrambled out of the car, and as the Rolls paused at the gates she ran over, and tapped on the rear window. It was tinted, so that

she couldn't see inside, but she knew there was
someone in there.

'Mr Preston? Could I just have a word with you?'
No response. The gates were opening—there must be
some sort of automatic system operated by the
chauffeur—and the car began to move forward again.
Furious at being ignored, she ran after it, heedless of
the butler's earlier threat to call the police. 'Mr
Preston . . . ?'

The car drew to a majestic halt in front of the house,
and she rapped on the window again, harder this time.
The driver's door opened, and the chauffeur climbed
out, his eyes glaring with angry belligerence that she
should have dared to touch his precious charge.

'Oy! What do you think you're doing? Clear off!'

'I want to speak to Mr Preston,' she countered
forcefully—the man was built like a bull, but she certainly wasn't going to let him intimidate her.

'What, at this time of night? Don't be ridiculous!
If you want to see him, you make a proper ap-
pointment through his secretary.'

'I've tried that,' she retorted. 'It doesn't work.'

'No—well, I'm not surprised.' The chauffeur's
glance was every bit as condescending as the butler's
had been. 'Mr Preston's a very busy man—he don't
have time for every bit of rag-tag as wants to see him.
And you're *certainly* not to be bothering him now.
Go on, get off with you, before I have Sanderson get
the police.'

He took a menacing step towards her, but she stood
her ground defiantly. 'I'm not going till I see Mr
Preston,' she insisted, raising her fist to give the
window the kind of pounding that even the elusive

E.J. Preston couldn't ignore. But as she moved to strike the glass it melted down, and she found herself staring into the coldest pair of blue eyes she had ever seen.

'What is the problem, Dalton?'

'I'm sorry, sir.' The chauffeur's instant deference suggested to Andrea that he was in terror that the slightest fault would earn him instant dismissal. 'There's a young lady here.'

'Apparently so.' Those eyes drifted over her in chilling indifference. 'What do you want?'

Ludicrously, every word of the impeccable little speech she had been rehearsing for the past two days had completely deserted her. As she stood there gaping, he climbed out of the car. Instinctively she fell back a pace, gazing up at him with startled eyes— as much at finding herself actually overtopped by so many inches as in astonishment at finding herself at last face to face with the man she had been pursuing for so many weeks.

There were only a few hazy photographs of him in existence—he guarded his privacy well—and none of them had warned her that he would prove quite so disconcertingly good-looking in the flesh. Those bones had been sculpted by an artist; the forehead was high and intelligent, the cheekbones arrogantly slanting, the nose slightly aquiline, the jaw strong and uncompromising. But it was his mouth that fascinated her; there was something intriguingly sensual about it that sent an odd little shimmer of heat down her spine.

He had clearly been out for the evening; his black dinner-jacket was cut with all the expensive elegance she would have expected, and his shirt was pure silk.

But there was no hint of softness about his body—
every inch of him was lean, hard muscle, and she felt
her mouth go suddenly dry.

'Well?'

She swallowed hard, embarrassed to realise that she
had been staring. 'I . . . I wanted to speak to you for
a few minutes,' she stumbled awkwardly.

'What about?'

The note of cool disinterest in his voice stung her
into annoyance. He was treating her as if she were
some irritating nuisance to be brushed aside with as
little trouble as possible. 'About the pollution and destruction your factories are pouring out,' she rapped,
her icy tone a match for his. 'Though I don't suppose
you give a damn, so long as they're making a profit
for you.'

'If you believe that,' he responded, quite unperturbed by her attack, 'why are you wasting my time?'

'Because you have to put a stop to it! Don't you
realise what's happening to the newts in Peacham
Wood?'

'No—but I feel sure you're going to tell me.'

'They're failing to breed, that's what.' So he thought
it was funny, did he? 'They're being slowly poisoned
to death—by you.'

'Really? And no doubt you have evidence of that?'

'It's all right here.' She held out the report. 'The
newts are just an indicator of the kind of damage
that's being caused. My students have been working
on it as a research project, and collated all the results.
It won't take you very long to read it,' she added,
afraid of putting him off.

But he spared the slim document just one brief, disparaging glance. 'I see. Well, I would suggest you send it to my secretary, who will forward it to the relevant department,' he responded dismissively. 'Now if you will excuse me . . . ?' He turned away from her, indicating clearly that as far as he was concerned the conversation was at an end.

Her anger boiled over. 'No, I will *not* send it to your secretary,' she declared, pushing herself resolutely in front of him again. 'I want you to read it yourself—now.'

Those ice-blue eyes surveyed her with arrogant contempt, but before he could speak a soft, petulant voice interrupted. 'E.J., what's going on? Aren't we going inside? I'm cold.' A vision of loveliness in a shimmering pink evening gown stepped from the back of the Rolls. It was small wonder that she was cold, Andrea reflected tartly, since only her artlessly tumbled blonde curls covered her bare shoulders. She blinked at Andrea in slightly vacuous surprise. 'Who's this?'

'Nobody,' was his insulting explanation as he slid his arm around the girl's dainty waist to draw her to his side.

She glanced at Andrea with pity in her eyes, as if more than ready to believe that anyone who had to wear such a dowdy old raincoat must indeed be a nobody. 'Is it something to do with business?' she queried, pouting prettily up at E.J. 'You're not going to have to go to work *now*, are you?'

He laughed, pinching her cheek. 'At this time of night, and with you here, my precious?' he teased lightly. 'Of course not.'

Andrea's jaw tightened. 'I'm sorry to have bothered you,' she ground out, her tone clearly conveying her contempt for his scale of priorities—and, coincidentally, his taste in women. 'But you haven't heard the last of this, I can assure you of that. I'll stop you somehow.'

He lifted one dark, level eyebrow in cool mockery. 'How very melodramatic,' he drawled, an inflexion of sardonic amusement in his voice. 'However, if that raggle-taggle army you had with you the other day is the best you can muster, I don't think I have much to fear.'

'Oh, so you *did* notice us?' she flashed back at him. 'The way you ignored us, it seemed as if we were lucky you didn't just order your chauffeur to drive right over us!'

A faint hint of a smile seemed to be lurking at one corner of his mouth. 'I considered it,' he conceded, deliberately provocative. 'But it would have been so terribly messy.'

She glared at him, not at all willing to appreciate his sense of humour. 'There might not be many of us, but we can make sure you have to listen to us,' she threatened wildly. 'We're not just going to go away.'

He shrugged his wide shoulders, bored with the conversation. 'Suit yourself,' he responded, stepping past her. 'But now, much as I have enjoyed our discussion, I regret that I cannot spare any more time this evening.'

That really was the last straw! Storming past him, she plumped herself down on the top step. 'I'm staying right here until you read this report,' she vowed, reckless in her fury.

That laser-sharp gaze seemed to pierce right through her. 'I'm afraid that would be inconvenient,' he responded with unruffled calm. 'I should have to request Dalton to remove you.'

She cast a quick, anxious glance at the burly chauffeur, hovering behind his employer, but she tilted up her chin in bold defiance. 'I'm not moving,' she reiterated, challenging him.

He responded with a weary sigh. 'Have it your own way. Thank you, Dalton.'

Andrea squawked in alarm as the chauffeur stepped in, lifting her clean off her feet with no regard for her dignity, and carrying her kicking and screaming back down the drive. E.J. Preston had already disappeared into the house, his arm still around the air-head blonde, not even bothering to watch as his instructions were carried out.

'Let me go!' she protested furiously. 'I'll have you up for assault!'

The man's face was grim as he set her down on the pavement. 'And don't try no more tricks,' he warned stolidly. 'Mr Preston don't want to be disturbed no more tonight.'

Speechless, she watched as the gates were slammed shut on her. She could just bet Mr Preston didn't want to be disturbed—it was more than evident how *he* proposed to entertain himself for the rest of the evening! It had never ceased to amaze her that apparently intelligent men could be attracted to women

with no more between their ears than the latest shade
of nail-varnish.

Not that she cared what he chose to do in his private
life, of course, she reminded herself with disdain. She
was interested only in stopping him polluting the environment. And that wasn't going to be an easy task—
he didn't seem to give a damn.

CHAPTER TWO

'YOU'VE done *what*?' Andrea, rudely awakened in the middle of the night by Brian calling and throwing stones up at her window, sent up a desperate prayer that she would find out she was still dreaming.

'We've got him—he's in the back of the van.' Brian's voice was taut with excitement. 'Come on, hurry up—let us in. We're going to put him in that old store-room in the basement—you know, the one next to the boiler-room. Quick, before someone comes along.'

'I'll be right down,' she assured him grimly, and, pausing only to pull on a pair of jeans and an old sweater, she raced down the stairs.

The faculty's battered transit van was parked by the door, and she was confronted by a circle of eager, anxious faces that parted silently to let her through. The back door of the van stood open, and on the floor, face down, his wrists roughly tied behind his back, was E.J. Preston. He was wearing a similar dinner-jacket to the one he had had on the week before, when she had gone to his house.

'What have you *done*?' she breathed, horrified. 'You have to let him go, right this minute. You can't *kidnap* him, for goodness' sake!'

'We've done it!' Brian pointed out proudly. 'And there's not a mark on him, either. We used that gas my friend got, and it worked like a charm. He's slept like a baby all the way from London.'

'You're mad! You'll get into terrible trouble.' She scrambled into the van, anxiously bending over the unconscious figure on the floor. He seemed to be breathing well enough, but his skin was very pale. Almost unconsciously she reached out her hand, and stroked back a strand of jet-black hair that had fallen over his face.

A wave of pity caught at her heart. He looked so vulnerable and defenceless lying there, that awful rope around his wrists, all that proud, arrogant strength subdued. Tears sprang to the backs of her eyes. 'You've got to let him go,' she pleaded.

'As soon as he's agreed to our demands,' Brian insisted firmly. 'Come on, everyone, give me a hand. Careful—he's heavy. Roger, you take his feet.'

She stood by, watching helplessly as they lifted him from the van. It took six of them to carry him into the hall of residence, and down the stairs to the little-used store-room Brian had chosen. He must have been busy, Andrea reflected acidly—he had brought in a spare bed, and set it up against the wall. The room had no windows, but it did have a tiny washroom that was used by the cleaners in term-time, which made it ideal for his purpose.

'You ought to at least take his jacket off,' Andrea protested as they laid him down on the bed. 'It'll get all creased with him lying there.'

Brian laughed. 'What a thing to be fussing about! He's probably got hundreds of the things. But go on, if you must. Then help me fix this chain.'

Andrea stared at him in horror. 'You're not going to chain him to the wall!' she protested.

'We have to,' he insisted. 'He might wake up any minute, and I wouldn't fancy being around if he gets loose—he's a martial arts expert.'

'*What*? You never told me that.'

'I read it somewhere,' he explained a little sheepishly. 'He's a tenth dan Akaido champion, or something.'

She rolled her fine grey eyes heavenwards. 'Brilliant! Of all the people to pick on...! But even so, you can't chain him up. I wouldn't do that to a dog!'

He slanted her an impatient glance. 'Look, whose side are you on?' he demanded. 'If he gets away before we're ready to let him go, there'll be hell to pay. It'll look as if we're just ordinary criminals, kidnapping him for a ransom—no one'll believe the truth. Do you want us all to go to prison?'

'That's exactly what you deserve! I ought to call the police right now.'

But it was the sight of the pale, apprehensive young faces of her students that stopped her. She couldn't escape the fact that she was to a certain extent responsible for them, and it was partly her fault that they had got themselves into this scrape—she should have guessed that Brian would go ahead with his crazy scheme, and should have done more to argue against him.

Brian sensed her wavering, and pressed home his advantage. 'But you won't, will you?' he coaxed, slipping an arm around her waist.

She shook him off with an angry shrug. 'No, I won't,' she agreed tersely. 'But I just hope you're right about this only taking a couple of hours. What if he won't agree to do what you want?'

'Of course he'll agree,' he assured her with cheerful confidence. 'He won't have any choice.'

'Hmm.' After her one brief encounter with E.J. Preston, she took leave to doubt that.

She could do nothing but watch as Brian and Roger fastened a stout steel manacle around his wrist, and padlocked it to a length of chain wrapped around one of the thick central-heating pipes that ran along the wall. It allowed him just enough range of movement to reach the washroom, but he wouldn't be able to get to the door.

When they had finished, she insisted on checking for herself that the manacle wasn't too tight, and then settled a pillow comfortably under his head, unable to resist the temptation to stroke that jet-black hair one last time before she reluctantly left the bedside.

One last glance around the windowless little cell made her shudder. Imagine waking up alone in a place like this, to find yourself chained to the wall, not knowing who had captured you or what their intentions were! Guilt and pity twisted like a knife in her heart as the heavy door was shut and locked on him.

'Surely he should have woken up by now?' Andrea glanced anxiously at her watch. 'It's been more than three hours.'

Brian shrugged his shoulders in a dismissive gesture, but Andrea could tell that he was worried. 'It probably takes longer for the effects of the gas to wear off with some people than with others. And it did take rather a lot to put him out,' he added wryly. 'It was a good job we decided to use it—we'd never have got him any other way.'

'Just how sure are you it's safe?' she queried, frowning. 'What if he's got a heart condition or something that we don't know about?' She rose decisively to her feet. 'Give me the key,' she demanded. 'I'm going back down to have another look at him.'

He shook his head, a mulish expression around his thin mouth. 'You'll let him go,' he accused.

'I can't if you keep the key to that disgusting manacle thing, can I?' she pointed out, holding out her hand.

Reluctantly he passed over the door key, and she hurried down the stairs to the basement. It was almost morning—the others had all gone home to bed, but she had known that she wouldn't sleep a wink after what had happened. They had checked the prisoner every half-hour, but as he had shown no signs of stirring she had grown more and more concerned.

Unlocking the door cautiously, she pushed it open, and peered inside. There was no sound from the bed— he was still lying in exactly the same position as when they had left him. Closing and locking the door behind her, she swiftly crossed the room, and bent over the still form. His eyelids didn't so much as flicker, and his breathing was very shallow—if he was breathing at all.

Suddenly really worried, she put out her hand to touch his chest—and found herself grasped by the wrist and twisted over and down on to the bed in one swift, startling movement. That hard-muscled body was on top of her, pinning her to the thin mattress,

and those ice-cold eyes were glinting down into hers
from inches above her face.

'Well, well. Not even wearing a mask,' he sneered.
'Very careless. Or was it intentional?'

'I . . . I thought you were still asleep,' she gasped,
panting for breath. 'I was worried about you.'

'How touching.' He laughed without humour. 'Tell
me, do your friends always put you in the front line
while they keep safely out of danger? Or are you the
only one intent on becoming a martyr for your cause?'

'None of us is planning on being a martyr,' she
tossed back with as much dignity as she could manage
in the circumstances—every inch of her body was
crushed beneath his, creating an illusion of intimacy
that was making her heartbeat race. 'We just want
you to listen.'

'You're not exactly asking very politely,' he pointed
out, jerking the chain that held his wrist. 'I suppose
it's too much to hope that you've got the key to this
on your person?'

'No, I haven't.'

His eyes narrowed, glinting in shrewd speculation.
'No? But then you would say that, wouldn't you?
Maybe I should search you—I'm not likely to get a
chance as good as this again.'

With a thud of panic she recognised his intention,
and tried to escape, but found her wrist twisted back
in a way that prevented her from moving at all. She
gasped, gritting her teeth in pain. 'You're hurting me,'
she protested.

'My heart bleeds,' he countered grimly, shifting his
weight from her.

He began his search at the neck of her hand-knitted sweater, and she tensed, her body rigid as she felt his hand run down over her body, insolently searching every inch. Then with an effortless movement he forced her over on to her stomach, and completed the examination.

'Satisfied?' she spat, her face muffled by the pillow.

He slanted her a look of sardonic mockery as he let her go. 'Hardly. But in the circumstances, sex isn't exactly on my agenda.'

She sat up on the edge of the bed, regarding him with defiant hostility as she rubbed her sore wrist. And she had been feeling sorry for him! He was about as vulnerable as a coiled cobra—and as dangerous. 'There was no need for you to do that,' she protested, her cheeks scarlet with humiliation. 'I told you I didn't have the key.'

He laughed coldly. 'She's offended! You attack me with some kind of knock-out gas, you kidnap me, chain me up, and you expect me to behave like a gentleman? Sister, you're unique!'

She tilted up her chin. 'If you'd just taken the trouble to listen to us, none of this need have happened,' she countered, too angry to attempt to explain that she hadn't been responsible for abducting him—he probably wouldn't have believed her anyway. 'It was because you ignored us that we were forced to take desperate measures.'

He lifted one dark eyebrow. 'And just how far are you prepared to go with these desperate measures?' he enquired, his voice soft and very controlled. 'You must have known that I'd be able to identify you, at least—even if you'd taken the precaution of wearing a mask, that carrot-red mop of yours is pretty un-forgettable. So if you're not planning to be a martyr, and go to prison for this—as you undoubtedly will—you must be planning to kill me. What's your idea? A kangaroo court, without benefit of defending advocate, and then a summary execution as an example to others?'

'Of course not!' she protested, aghast. 'We're going to let you go. All we want you to do is read our report on the effect of the toxins you're emitting from your factory chimney. You just have to sign it, while we take some photographs for the papers.'

'Oh really?' His voice was ripe with cynicism. 'That's all?'

'Yes, that's all. I'll get the report—it's upstairs. I told you before, it won't take you very long to read it . . .'

'Don't bother.' A voice like a whiplash cut her short.

She stared at him. 'But as soon as you've read it, and signed it, we'll let you go,' she reiterated. 'I promise.'

'I don't do anything under coercion,' he responded coolly.

'But . . .' Her eyes sparked with frustration. 'Look, we'll drive you back to London—you'll be home before anyone hardly knows you're gone. I'm sorry we've put you to this inconvenience . . .'

His response was entirely unexpected. Sitting up very straight on the hard bed, he crossed his legs beneath him and placed his hands against his knees, palms upwards. His eyes focused on a point on the far wall, and he began to breathe, long and deep—ignoring her presence as if she weren't there.

Andrea stood staring at him in bewilderment. She had expected him to be angry, of course—he had every right to be. But she had hoped that he might at least be open to some sort of persuasion. But it was as if he had switched off completely from his surroundings, erecting a barrier that she didn't know how to deal with.

So what did they do now? she asked herself, perplexed. She had an uncomfortable feeling that in any clash of wills E.J. Preston would prove a formidable opponent. Of course, it shouldn't be that way—by the rules of logic, they had the upper hand. But E.J. Preston was the kind of man who wrote his own rules—whatever the circumstances.

'Have it your own way,' she shrugged at length, turning to the door. 'I'll fetch you something to eat.'

'No.'

She turned back to him in surprise—she hadn't expected an answer. He was still sitting motionless, not even looking at her, but she could sense a power emanating from him—a power that made her nervous. 'What do you mean?' she queried.

'Water,' he stated unequivocally. 'Don't bring any food—I won't eat it.'

'But... We're not going to poison you or anything,' she protested bemused.

Those blue eyes turned on her, seeming to chill the marrow in her bones. 'I'm not going to eat anything,' he reiterated calmly. 'Not until you let me go.'

'Oh—you're going to starve yourself to death?' she challenged, her voice laced with sarcasm. 'Very clever.'

'If I die, it will be your responsibility,' he spelled out with icy precision. 'Do you want to take that kind of risk?'

She could feel herself beginning to tremble under the laser sharpness of that penetrating gaze. This was ridiculous—this man was helpless, chained to the wall, and yet he was the one dictating terms. Her sympathy had certainly been wasted on him, she reflected tartly—even unconscious he could probably have outsmarted them all.

'Have it your own way,' she snapped. 'We're only trying to do something positive to protect the environment, and stop people like you messing it up for your own greedy profit.'

He turned his eyes to focus on the wall again. 'Try not to talk in slogans all the time,' he advised in a tone of utter boredom. 'It debases the art of conversation.'

His sheer arrogance almost made her gasp. She had never met anyone so . . . impossible! Well, if he didn't want to eat, that was his look-out—she certainly wasn't going to beg him! Turning on her heel, she unlocked the door and stalked out, slamming it hard behind her and locking it with a snap.

Brian was sprawled on the narrow single bed in her cluttered flatlet upstairs. He glanced up in surprise as she walked in, her face taut. 'What's the matter?' he demanded at once. 'He's all right, isn't he?'

'Oh, he's all right,' she assured him through clenched teeth. 'He's wide awake now—you'd never think he'd breathed so much as a whiff of any knock-out gas in his life! He's doing yoga.'

'He's *what*?'

'You heard. He's refused to even look at the report, and he says he won't eat anything until we let him go.'

He looked at her with a suspicious frown. 'What did you say to him?' he demanded.

'I told him that we'd let him go as soon as he'd read the report,' she responded, her patience strained to the edge. 'He said he wouldn't do anything under coercion.'

Brian laughed drily. 'Well, I hardly expected him to give in at once,' he declared with unabated confidence. 'As for the not eating, he's just bluffing. He probably hasn't had time to get hungry yet, but you wait till he's gone a few more hours without food—he'll soon change his tune.'

'I doubt it. You said he's a martial arts expert—aren't they trained in self-control?'

He scoffed. 'We'll see. Give it a bit longer, and then do him some bacon and eggs—I bet once he smells that he'll find his appetite soon enough.'

'Right.' She smiled in grim relish. 'I think I've got some in the fridge—I've got some eggs, anyway.' She cast a wry glance around the untidy little kitchenette. 'I really must do something about this place,' she mused vaguely. 'I never seem to have enough time to keep it tidy.'

But evidently E.J. Preston was immune to the appetising aroma of bacon and eggs. He had ignored Andrea totally when she took the tray in, setting it down on a low table beside the bed. She had brought a glass of mineral water, as well as a cup of coffee—more as a deliberate taunt than in obedience to his instructions. But when she went back for the tray an hour later, only the water had been touched. The bacon and eggs had congealed on the plate, and the coffee was stone-cold.

And he hadn't moved. He was still in that yoga position, his spine very straight, his concentration unwavering as she walked across the room. She eyed him warily, careful not to get too close—the memory of the way he had searched her so thoroughly before was still burned into her brain.

He seemed so immobile that she started in shock as those chilling blue eyes turned to her just as she was about to pick up the tray. 'Oh . . . I'm sorry,' she found herself apologising foolishly. 'Don't you want anything to eat at all? I could do you some toast?'

A hint of mockery curved that controlled mouth. 'I told you I wasn't going to eat anything,' he reminded her, a sardonic inflexion in his voice. 'You're wasting your time trying to tempt me.'

'I wouldn't dream of trying to tempt you,' she retorted, retreating into icy dignity. 'You can starve yourself to death for all I care. After all, what's your life to the hundreds who are suffering because of the poisons you're throwing out into the atmosphere?'

'What indeed?' he agreed cordially. 'And the end justifies the means?'

'In certain cases,' she responded, hesitating only for the briefest second; it wasn't a proposition she supported, but she wasn't going to let him see that she had anything less than a solid conviction.

He laughed without humour. 'Another slogan—and the self-acquittal of all terrorists,' he taunted. 'Who gave you the right to decide matters of life and death?'

'Who gave it to you?' she flashed back, her eyes sparking. 'If you call us terrorists, what does that make someone who puts thousands of lives at risk?'

He acknowledged her point with a nod of his head, a flicker of a smile lurking around that disturbingly sensual mouth. 'And so once again we come to the same impasse,' he concluded. 'An interesting game, isn't it?'

'I don't think it's a game,' she managed stiffly. 'It's very important to me.'

'I would hope that it is. I wouldn't like to think that you were prepared to allow another human being to die for something you regarded as trivial.'

'I don't think you *are* a human being,' she snapped, losing her composure altogether. 'You're a . . . an iceberg—with a computer for a brain.'

That seemed to really amuse him. 'Well done, Carrots,' he approved. 'You're really quite intelligent—when you stop mouthing slogans like a wax dummy.'

'Oh... Rats to you!' On that childish expletive, she snatched up the tray and marched over to the door, angered all the more by having to balance it clumsily with one hand as she turned the key. He was still laughing as she locked the door behind her.

Pale morning sunlight was filtering through the curtains, making it hard to sleep. Andrea rolled over, impatiently punching the pillow into a better shape. She desperately wanted to sleep, but her mind was too wound up with worry. What were they going to do about the man in the tiny basement cell downstairs?

Any hope she might have had that the whole thing could be settled quickly, and that with his safe and speedy return the consequences of his abduction might not be too severe, was already gone. By now the hunt would already be on—and E.J. Preston was ruthless enough to see them all in prison for a very long time.

But Brian had been right—if they released him without achieving what they wanted, it would all be for nothing. Well, all right, if that was the way he wanted to play it, she decided, gritting her teeth. At least they could make it worthwhile—their trial would give massive publicity to the pollution issue, so they would achieve their objective after all.

But what were they going to do if he went on refusing to eat? A small shiver ran through her at the memory of those chilling blue eyes. And the way he had sat there, so still, so controlled . . . What kind of opponent had they taken on . . . ?

At last she fell asleep, but her dreams were troubled—she was in a courtroom, and E.J. Preston was the judge; but for some reason she was performing an erotic striptease, while he sat there watching her with icy contempt. 'You're wasting your time trying to tempt me . . .'

It was midday when she woke, after just a few hours' restless sleep. But she knew it was a waste of time staying in bed any longer, so reluctantly she got up, pulling on her old jeans and another sweater, and went along to the common-room at the end of the corridor, where some of the students were drinking coffee and talking in subdued voices. The early edition of the local evening paper was already out, and the headline was strident—'Missing Businessman Alert'.

'Oh, rats!' muttered Andrea, glancing through the story beneath the photograph. E.J.'s disappearance had sparked a massive man-hunt; helicopters and troops were searching, airports and shipping were being checked. It seemed that the IRA were the chief suspects.

'Maybe we should let him go,' Roger suggested in shaken apprehension.

Andrea rounded on him, her eyes sparking. 'It's a bit late now,' she rapped tartly. 'You should have thought of the consequences before you did it.'

'But Brian said——'

'Oh, don't tell me about it,' she cut him off with an impatient wave of her hand. 'How is he, anyway? Has he deigned to eat anything after all?'

'No.' Roger shook his head. 'It's really weird. He hasn't moved an inch all morning—I'd swear he's not even blinking. He just sits there, not even looking at you—it's like he's on another plane.'

'I'm not going in there again,' added one of the girls with a shudder. 'He scares me. It's like he could strike you dead just by looking at you.'

'I...I'd better go and check on him again,' Andrea suggested, though her heart was already beginning to beat a little unsteadily.

'Rather you than me,' declared Roger, handing over the key.

This was getting silly, Andrea reflected as she walked down the stairs. How could they all be afraid of him? He couldn't do them any real harm—he was chained to the wall, for goodness' sake! But nevertheless, she paused outside the basement door, drawing a few

deep, steadying breaths. Then she turned the key, and
pushed the door open.

E.J. was still sitting exactly as he had been the last
time she had seen him. And she remembered at once
why they were all afraid of him; that air of almost
supernatural menace that emanated from him seemed
to chill the whole room, in spite of the heat from the
boiler-room next door.

She had drawn the door shut behind her, locking
it, leaning against it as she watched him. Roger was
right—he didn't even seem to be blinking. But then
quite suddenly those cold blue eyes turned to her, and
she felt her heart thud in alarm.

'Hello, Carrots,' he greeted her, that soft, controlled voice making her shiver. 'I was beginning to
wonder when you'd be back—I was getting a little
tired of waiting.'

She had to struggle to retain some semblance of
composure. 'You surely don't expect me to believe
you're pleased to see me?' she returned, her voice
commendably even.

'Why not? You're considerably more interesting
than those porridge-faced dizzards you've been
sending in to gawp at me all morning. And while I
couldn't say you're exactly beautiful, you're a great
deal better to look at than these four walls.'

Her eyes flashed in indignation. 'You really know
how to pay a girl compliments, don't you?' she protested, stung.

He laughed in lazy mockery. 'This is hardly the
situation in which I normally pay compliments,' he
pointed out. 'Besides, I don't think you're vain enough
to believe a pack of flattering lies. Nevertheless, you

are good to look at.' He let his eyes drift down over her in a leisurely appraisal, lingering intimately over every slender inch, and she found herself vividly recalling the way he had touched her earlier in the day.

She tilted up her chin, regarding him with haughty disdain. 'If you think sexual harassment will get you anywhere . . .' she scorned.

'Sexual harassment?' A faint smile flickered at the corners of his mouth. 'You call it sexual harassment when a man looks at you? Although I suppose that's not altogether surprising, if that wimp with the mousy hair is any example of the sort of lovers you usually pick—he wouldn't know how to handle you in a million years.'

'I've no wish to be "handled", as you put it,' she retorted crisply. 'I see you've finished your water.' She forced herself away from the door, and walked briskly across the room. 'I'll fetch you some more.'

He had been sitting so still that she perhaps hadn't been fully on her guard. But as she reached down her hand to pick up the glass, he moved with alarming swiftness, slipping off the bed and catching her wrist in a loop of his chain, dragging her ruthlessly against him. She stared up at him, her eyes wide with shock.

'But then maybe you've never been handled properly,' he taunted smoothly. 'Would you mind if I demonstrate?'

It was an entirely rhetorical question—he had no intention of waiting on her permission. As she stood transfixed, his arm slid around her waist, curving her against him, and the subtle musky scent of his skin filled her senses. Every ounce of reason was screaming at her to push him away, but her will was no longer under her control—it had been taken over by the hypnotic power of those laser-blue eyes.

Slowly he bent his head, his mouth brushing softly, sensuously over hers. She caught her breath on a startled little gasp, her heartbeat faltering. His tongue had fickered into the corner of her trembling lips, parting them to sweep languorously over the sensitive inner membranes, and then with unhurried ease sought the soft inner sweetness, plundering in a deliberately flagrant exploration into the most secret depths, coaxing and inciting a response.

She felt herself grow dizzy, melting in helpless surrender into his arms, even as she cursed herself for a crazy fool for letting him play this game on her. She knew what he was doing; he wasn't remotely attracted to her, but he had sensed her weakness, and was exploiting it quite ruthlessly to persuade her to let him go. But that knowledge couldn't protect her; she had never been kissed like this, and she didn't want it ever to end.

By the time he lifted his head, she felt as if she had moved into another lifetime. But he was smiling down into her eyes with lazy mockery. 'I think I've proved my point,' he murmured.

She drew back from him, though still shackled to him by that chain around her wrist; her eyes blazed angry defiance as she gazed up at him, humiliation painting her cheeks scarlet. 'It . . . it won't do you any good,' she insisted unsteadily, wiping the back of her hand across her mouth in a vain attempt to wipe away the memory of that kiss. 'We're not going to let you go until . . . until you've read that report.'

His mocking laughter taunted her. 'Ah, but then maybe I'm not in a particular hurry for you to let me go,' he mused, jerking on the chain to pull her close again. 'This is proving to be a remarkably entertaining interlude.'

But this time she was ready for him, putting her hand up against his hard chest in a swift gesture of defence, leaning away from him. 'It's up to you,' she stated, keeping her voice commendably cool. 'We can keep you here for as long as necessary—the police will be looking for you in all the wrong places. I wonder how your business will be managing without you?'

'Good one,' he acknowledged, still smiling. 'This is definitely proving entertaining.'

'I'm beginning to think you're just crazy,' she snapped. 'And you're hurting my wrist.'

'How do you think it feels for me?' he growled, suddenly alarmingly savage, his face inches above her own. 'You've chained me up like a dog. Do you think I'm just going to let you get away with that? You've mistaken your man. You'll pay—believe me on that.'

He unwound the chain from her wrist, and she backed away from him, nursing her bruised skin tenderly. She had been right to be afraid of him; he was a very dangerous opponent, prepared to use any kind of ruthless strategy to win the game.

She ought to have been more careful—what was it he had seen in her that had made him think that she would be vulnerable to that kind of attack? Well, she wasn't going to let it happen again—she wasn't going to give this hateful man the satisfaction of letting him see any sign of weakness.

'We'll cross that bridge when we come to it,' she retorted, tossing her hair back over her shoulder. 'What would you like for dinner? How about a nice, thick, juicy fillet steak, cooked rare, oozing with juice?'

His lips quirked into a smile of appreciative humour. 'Still trying to tempt me, Carrots?' he enquired mockingly. 'You won't succeed—at least, not that way. Now if you were to offer me your body...?'

Her eyes flashed, but she managed to keep her anger firmly under control. Stooping quickly, she picked up his drinking-glass from the floor, and moved back out of his reach. 'I'll get one of the others to bring you some water.'

'No—bring it yourself,' he insisted.

She returned him a haughty glare, and turned on her heel, marching over to the door and letting herself out.

It was only with the door safely closed and locked behind her that she felt able to breathe properly. Her heartbeat was racing so fast that she felt light-headed, and her lips still retained a physical memory of that kiss, her body could still feel the impact of that strong embrace.

But she could have no illusions; it had all been a game to him, taunting her with kisses that meant nothing to him—because he knew they would mean far too much to her. But she was in no danger of succumbing, she assured herself resolutely; she only had to recall the way he had treated her last week, in front of that silly little blonde bimbo girlfriend of his. In fact, she reminded herself with a quirk of wry humour, he had rated her only slightly better than gazing at the four walls!

He had been right that she wasn't so vain as to be taken in by a pack of flattering lies—her own mirror told her every day that she was no beauty. But she hadn't given up on men entirely—she still retained a shred of hope that there was at least one man out there whose taste ran to tall, slim, intelligent women, rather than bits of fluff. The passing years might have strained that optimism a little, but she was still only twenty-seven years old, after all—there was plenty of time.

But one thing was absolutely certain, she asserted firmly—E.J. Preston was not that man!

CHAPTER THREE

'HE THREW it at me!' Roger reappeared in the upstairs common-room, a large wet patch spread across the front of his shirt, holding the broken shards of a drinking-glass in his hand. 'He said you're to take it to him,' he added to Andrea.

She felt her cheeks grow a little pale. The others all turned to stare at her. 'Why you?' demanded Brian, frowning in suspicion—he had arrived while Andrea had been downstairs. 'What's going on?'

'I... don't know,' she responded with difficulty. 'Maybe I'd... better do what he wants.'

'I'll come with you,' Brian decided grimly. 'I don't trust him.'

'You mean you don't trust me,' she countered, her voice taut with irritation. How on earth could she ever have let any sort of relationship grow between them, even the limited one that existed? Sometimes he could be so ridiculously pompous and self-important that she was almost tempted to laugh at him.

'No, no,' he assured her earnestly. 'I know you wouldn't let the cause down. But it would pay to be extra-careful with him—he's very clever, and there's no telling what sort of trick he might get up to.'

'I think we should all go down,' Roger suggested, sounding less than enthusiastic. 'It's time we put all our cards on the table.'

'Right,' agreed Brian, looking faintly relieved that he wasn't going to be called upon to put his courage to the test unsupported. 'Drea, bring the report.'

This was really rather ridiculous, Andrea reflected as they all trooped down the stairs—anyone would have thought it was a fire-breathing dragon they had chained up in the basement, not an ordinary man. But as Brian opened the door, and she found herself once again in his presence, she was reminded all too clearly that E.J. Preston was not an ordinary man— he was a very *extraordinary* one.

A glow of angry fire burned in his eyes as he watched them all huddle into the room. 'Well, now, what's this?' he sneered with icy disdain. 'A deputation?'

Brian took the file containing the report from Andrea's hands. 'We've come to——'

'The only thing I want to hear from you,' the voice that cut him off was quiet with menace, 'is an apology. Unlock this damned chain, or I swear if I ever get my hands on you I'll throttle the life out of you.'

Brian looked slightly taken aback, but tried to stand his ground. 'We'll let you go as soon as you've read this,' he insisted, his voice a few quavers higher than its normal pitch. 'It's a detailed analysis of the pollutants being emitted by your factory...'

He stepped forward to hand over the report, holding it at arm's length, but the man on the bed simply regarded him with a look of searing contempt, making no attempt to take it from him. 'You snivelling little weasel,' he gibed, deliberately provocative. 'Look at you, standing there shaking in your shoes, when I can't even get near you. You make me sick!'

Brian swallowed hard, but persevered. 'All we want you to do——'

'I know what you want me to do. *She* told me.' That laser-sharp glance impaled Andrea as she tried in vain to hide behind the others. 'And I told her that I don't do anything under coercion. I'll see you all rot in hell first. Now get out of my sight, before I rip this chain out of the wall.'

He jerked on it, and for an awful second it seemed as though he really was strong enough to snap the steel links. Brian didn't wait to find out if he could— he scampered back out of the door like a scalded rabbit, the others hard on his heels.

Outside they all looked at each other sheepishly— five people, terrified of one man, chained to a wall. 'Well...' Brian cleared his throat. 'I think...we'd better go along with him,' he choked out. 'It wouldn't do to antagonise him.'

'You don't think perhaps we've antagonised him enough already?' interjected Andrea drily.

'Well, we don't have make it any worse! From now on, you're the only one to take food in to him.'

'Oh, great. Thank you very much.' Her eyes flashed in icy scorn. 'Leave it all to me, why don't you? All right—I'll wait on him. I just hope this doesn't go on too long!' She almost snatched the glass of water out of Roger's hand, and marched back into the room.

E.J. was sitting across the bed, leaning back against the wall, his hands folded behind his head, calmly waiting for her, knowing that she would come back. She glared at him, infuriated by the glint of mocking triumph in his eyes.

'There was no need to speak to Brian like that,' she snapped. 'I know he can be a bit wet at times, but he's very sincere.'

'Ha!' He shouted with laughter. 'You think I should be nice to him? This was all his idea, wasn't it? He was the one who attacked me—the coward's way, not even a fair fight. Besides, I told you to bring the water yourself. You'd better learn that when I say something I don't do it simply for the pleasure of hearing myself speak.'

She studied him warily from beneath her lashes. Just moments ago he had been ferociously angry, but now he was as cool as ever again. But she was beginning to suspect that his unpredictable mood-changes were very much under his control, a deliberate strategy to keep her off-balance. He was as dangerous as a cornered rattlesnake, and she would be wise to keep her guard up at all times.

'I've... brought your water,' she announced, somewhat unnecessarily.

'So I see.' There was an inflexion of sardonic humour in his voice. 'Why don't you bring it over here and put it down, then?'

She approached the bed warily, ready to dart back if he made the slightest move towards her. But he remained still, just watching her, that taunting smile hovering at the corners of his mouth. She set the glass down, and edged back out of his reach.

'There.' He was like a sleek cat toying with a trapped mouse. 'You see—if you do as you're told, everything's all right.'

She couldn't think of a single retort that he wasn't likely to turn against her. He was regarding her with

a lazy interest that made her feel acutely uncomfortable; she never knew how to handle him, nor
what to expect.

'Why do you wear such awful clothes?' he enquired in a tone of mild curiosity. 'Are you one of
those fierce women who believes that looking feminine
and attractive is a sell-out to the chauvinistic male
establishment?'

Her eyes sparked with indignation. 'No!' she protested, glancing down rather self-consciously at her
thick hand-knitted sweater and well-worn jeans. 'I
simply prefer to wear clothes that are ... practical and
comfortable.'

'It looks as if you're trying—not very success-
fully—to hide the fact that there's a woman's body
underneath. A rather good body, too,' he added with
a hint of reminiscence, 'A little slender for some tastes,
perhaps, but you've certainly got curves in all the right
places.'

She could feel a hot tinge of pink colour her cheeks,
but she tilted up her chin at a haughty angle. 'For
your information, I'm in the middle of a very important research project into the effect of heavy metals
on the human immune system. I don't have the time,
or the money, to prance around like a mannequin.
And besides, I happen to like this sweater—my mother
knitted it for me.'

'Ah ... Your mother.' He nodded sagely.

'And what's that supposed to mean?' she challenged, bridling.

'Oh, nothing.' His eyes were glinting in a way that
warned her that he was deliberately trying to needle

her for his own amusement. 'I'm sure she's an esti-
mable woman.'

'She is. And it's not very fair of you to mock her
when you haven't even met her.'

'Nothing could be further from my thoughts!' he
assured her blandly. 'So tell me about your family.
Do you have any brothers and sisters?'

'Three sisters,' she responded automatically, a little
bewildered by this sudden change in direction.

'And are they married?'

'Yes. Lizzie has three children, Marge has two and
Babs has just had her first baby.'

'Quite a crew,' he remarked. I'm surprised your
mother doesn't have all the knitting she can handle
just clothing them.'

'She likes to keep busy.' She was studying him sus-
piciously from beneath her lashes; she was quite sure
he wasn't leading her into this line of conversation
out of any real interest in her family. So what was he
up to?

'And what does your father do?' he asked, his tone
simply one of polite enquiry.

'He used to be a pharmacist. Unfortunately he had
to retire last year—he has trouble with his heart.'

'Oh, I see—I'm sorry.' But she couldn't help feeling
it was another snippet of information he was filing
away, to somehow use against her at some time in the
future. 'Haven't you ever felt the desire to emulate
your sisters? Or are you planning to remain forever
the maiden aunt?'

'Not particularly,' she informed him with lofty
dignity. 'But for the time being I prefer to give all my
attention to my career.'

'No love-affairs?'

'No!' she blurted out, caught off-balance by the unexpected twists in his questions.

'Never?' he persisted, a sly glint in those blue eyes.

Hot scarlet flamed in her cheeks. 'I . . . didn't say that.'

'But not at the moment, eh?' He was amused by her discomfiture. 'Not even that wimp with the mousy hair?'

'No.' She was struggling to regather the tattered shreds of her composure. 'Not that it's any of your business,' she objected somewhat belatedly.

'Oh, but it's a very interesting line of research,' he persisted with an air of scientific detatchment. 'What drives a woman to terrorism? Could it be, in some cases, sexual frustration?'

'I'm not a terrorist!' she retorted with some heat. 'And I'm not sexually frustrated, either.'

'And yet you claim you don't have a lover?'

'No, I don't. I don't need one—I'm perfectly happy the way I am.'

'Are you?' Those eyes were holding her with their mesmerising gaze so that she couldn't look away. 'It seems such a terrible waste—a woman who responds to a man's touch the way you do, sleeping alone at night. But maybe the problem is that you tower head and shoulders over all the men around you—and I don't mean just physically,' he added with dry humour.

Andrea stared at him helplessly; how was it that he could always touch a raw nerve with such unerring accuracy? She couldn't help it that she intimidated men—even if she could have pretended to be stupid, she couldn't pretend to be six inches shorter! But she wasn't going to concede the point.

'If you're referring to Brian,' she responded coldly, 'as a matter of fact he's *very* highly respected in his field. And his hair isn't mousy,' she added, rather undermining the dignity of her argument. 'It's light brown.'

He shouted with laughter. 'My apologies! But I'm glad to know he's not your lover—he'd be no match for you.'

'And you think you would be?' she challenged, fury making her reckless.

He smiled in mocking triumph, and she almost kicked herself; she had fallen into exactly the trap he had set for her. Slanting him a withering glare, she turned on her heel, and stalked over to the door. 'I'll bring you your dinner at six o'clock,' she tossed over her shoulder as she let herself out of the room. 'Enjoy your glass of water.'

At least she had managed to leave him chuckling in appreciation of her parting shot.

The others were more than willing to leave the task of waiting on their intimidating prisoner entirely to Andrea—a fact which she noted with considerable resentment. Going into that basement room alone had become like a private nightmare—facing those cold, taunting eyes, that soft, mocking voice . . .

He had maintained his refusal to eat. They had tried everything they could think of to tempt him—crisp pork chops with the crackling still on, Elaine's homemade steak and kidney pie—but everything had been left untouched. Most of the time he just sat on the

bed, in that meditative yoga position—he rarely even
lay down to go to sleep. But three times a day, at precisely the same time, he would go through a routine
of yoga exercises, some of which looked impossible.

As the days passed, Andrea was becoming increas-
ingly concerned. How long could a man go without
food? She could look up all the scientific data, but
figures on a page meant nothing when it came to a
living, breathing human being. When she was re-
duced to pleading with him, he just laughed.

'The solution is in your hands, Carrots. All you
have to do is let me go.'

'Why won't you just read the report?' she demanded, thoroughly exasperated. 'I've never known
such a stupid, obstinate...'

He was smiling in lazy mockery, enjoying pro-
voking her. 'Irritating, isn't it, when things don't go
according to plan?'

'*You're* irritating!' she snapped back. 'You're doing
this deliberately—the longer it's going on, the more
likely it is that we'll get a really stiff prison sentence
for kidnapping you.'

'Quite.'

'Doesn't it even bother you that the police are
wasting so much time looking for you?'

He lifted his wide shoulders in a gesture of indifference, that infuriatingly sardonic smile curving his
fascinating mouth. 'It's you that's holding me
prisoner,' he pointed out. 'Doesn't it bother you?'

'If you'd just do what we wanted...'

Those cold blue eyes glinted, and she knew she was
wasting her breath. The battle of wills that she had
feared was turning out exactly as she had predicted—

he was winning hands down. And there didn't seem to be a thing they could do about it; there was no way they could break that iron self-discipline.

'I just hope you don't find when you get back that your business has gone to rack and ruin without you,' she snapped tartly.

'Do you?' he countered, his eyes flickering with sardonic humour. 'Wouldn't you like to see the downfall of another dirty capitalist?'

'This isn't political,' she insisted with dignity. 'I've got nothing at all against capitalism. What I object to is the destruction of the environment. Surely it's possible to find ways of making manufacturing processes safer?'

'Of course it is,' he conceded.

'Well, then! Even if it's less economical in financial terms, surely it's better in the long run?'

He tilted his head to one side, regarding her with mild interest. 'Do you know, when you get carried away like that, you're almost beautiful?' he taunted provocatively. 'Your eyes light up like flame.'

She glared at him, her fury barely contained. 'I hate you!' she snarled. 'I hope your business *does* go broke!'

'Oh, I don't think it will,' he countered, maddeningly unperturbed. 'I have some very good staff, who are quite well able to take care of things while I'm away. In fact, it could turn out to be quite useful, having a few days without all the usual distractions that plague me. It's a rare pleasure to have so much time just for pure meditation.'

'I'm so glad we were able to oblige!' she rapped,

and, picking up the tray of untouched food, stalked from the room.

'We're going to have to let him go.' The group were sitting around upstairs in the common-room, drinking coffee. 'He isn't going to give in. This whole thing is turning into a complete fiasco.'

'Drea's right,' agreed Roger dismally. 'It's getting ridiculous. You can't turn on the telly or pick up a newspaper without it leaping out at you. I know the police are still sticking to the IRA theory, but sooner or later they're going to start following up other leads, and then they're going to come across our campaign.'

'And the Easter vac's almost over,' put in Elaine. 'The rest of the students will be back by the weekend— we won't be able to carry on like this then.'

'Well, it's up to you to vote on it, of course,' Brian remarked, feigning neutrality but unable to keep the edge of annoyance out of his voice. 'But don't forget, if we let him go now, it'll all have been for nothing. It's his fault it's dragged on—if he'd just co-operated, we could have let him go right away. Now we'll all more than likely go to prison.'

'You knew you were taking that risk when you dreamed up this crazy scheme,' Andrea reminded him tartly. 'Besides, it's been nearly a week now and he hasn't eaten a thing. He seems perfectly all right at the moment, but how much longer can we let it continue? I'm not going to have his death on my conscience.'

'What's getting into you?' retorted Brian, an unpleasant edge of sarcasm in his voice. 'Beginning to fancy him, are you?'

'No, of course not,' she protested, maybe a little too sharply. 'I never wanted to get involved with this in the first place—you dragged me into it. But now it's time to admit that he's got the better of us, and let him go.'

Brian scowled, reluctant to admit anything of the sort. 'I say we've been too soft on him,' he argued petulantly, 'letting him string us along like this. If we stopped giving him water, he'd soon come round.'

'No!' Andrea put down her coffee-cup, and rose decisively to her feet. 'It's over. Give me the key to the manacle—or I'll ring the police right now.'

'Yes,' Roger put in. 'Give her the key, Brian.'

Brian cast a challenging look around the group, but found no supporters. With a grunt of impatience he put his hand into his pocket. 'All right—have it your own way,' he conceded, handing over the key. 'Personally I think we could go on for at least another week, but if you lot want to chicken out...'

Andrea took the key from him, her feelings a strange mixture of relief and regret. She knew she had to set E.J. free, but that would also mean that she would never see him again—except perhaps in court.

Of course that was for the best, she told herself firmly. He had unsettled her emotions far more than any man she had ever known, but she knew all too well that he would never even have looked twice at her in any other circumstances. Over the past week she had allowed herself to slip into a kind of fantasy, accepting his pretence of interest as if it were real—but to let that go on any longer would be courting disaster.

For the last time, she walked down the stairs, and fitted the key into the lock—her hand was shaking so much it was difficult to turn the key. For a change, he was stretched out full-length on the bed, but he wasn't asleep—a gleam of ice-blue pierced across the room as soon as she opened the door.

'Good afternoon, Carrots.' The voice was mockingly polite. 'To what do I owe this pleasure? It certainly isn't dinnertime yet.'

'No.' She drew a long, steadying breath, but her voice was still shaking slightly. 'I . . . I've come to let you go.'

'Well, well!' He sat up, a smile curving the corners of his mouth. 'So you're finally admitting defeat?'

'Yes,' she retorted, trying for a tone of icy dignity. 'But only because we don't want to see you starve yourself to death.'

'How nice to know that you're so concerned about me,' he drawled, his voice heavy with irony.

She gritted her teeth, and walked across to the bed. Since that first day, she had managed to avoid getting too close to him—their sparring had been purely verbal. But now, although he held up his shackled wrist, he was deliberately drawing it back, until she was forced to lean right over him to unlock it. Her hands were still shaking—the more so with her acute awareness of that taut, muscular maleness so close to her—and it took her a few seconds even to get the key into the lock.

'I hope you're not as unsteady as this when you're conducting your experiments,' he taunted, fully aware of the effect he had on her. 'You'd be forever dropping things on the floor.'

'I . . . we . . . mostly use computer simulations now,' she informed him, her heart jumping around in a kind of panic. 'A lot of the materials are too dangerous to experiment with.'

'Ah.' He nodded sagely, easing his wrist as she at last managed to unfasten the manacle. To her horror, it had raised a fierce red weal on his skin.

'Oh, my goodness . . . I'm sorry. I never thought . . . We never meant . . .'

His soft laughter mocked her, and he caught her around the waist, drawing her down on to his lap. 'What's this?' he teased, putting up a hand to her cheek to lift one sparkling tear-drop on to the tip of his finger. 'Could it be that the ruthless terrorist possesses a woman's heart after all? Will you bathe my wounds with your tears?'

'I never wanted for you to be hurt,' she whispered brokenly. 'If I'd known . . . You never said . . .'

'Ah, well, I never was one to complain about small discomforts,' he quipped lightly. 'Besides, I was enjoying quite an amusing little interlude—I wasn't in any particular hurry for it to end.'

'But . . .' She cast a bemused glance around at the four ugly blank walls. 'You can't have been enjoying this.'

'Not this room, nó. But I knew I had the pleasure to look forward to every few hours of having you come into the room, my sweet terrorist.'

Her eyes flashed in angry resentment, trying in vain to pull away from him. 'Don't start talking like that again,' she protested. 'I'm letting you go—there's no need to play games any longer.'

'But I like playing games.' He was drawing her inexorably towards him, his warm breath fanning her cheek, his hand sliding up beneath her sweater to caress her bare back. 'Particularly these sort of games.'

'Let me go...' But her voice lacked conviction. 'Don't...'

His eyes glinted with lazy mockery. 'Have you forgotten?' he taunted softly. 'I warned you that I was going to make you pay. Look on this as the first instalment.'

His mouth came down on hers, moving with a slow, warm sensuality that coaxed her lips apart, and she groaned softly, powerless to defend herself. Since the first time he had kissed her she had been aching to feel the hard strength of his arms around her again. She knew it was fatal; he was only amusing himself, using her unwilling attraction to him as a cruel torment to punish her, but she had become a willing agent of her own destruction, an addict who would accept any degradation as the price of just one fix of her drug.

His hand had tangled into her hair, dragging her head down so that she was curved across his lap, helpless, and the other was stroking slowly down over the length of her spine and round her slender midriff, to rise beneath her sweater to brush against the soft underside of her breast. She whimpered in protest, but her traitorous body was responding beneath his expert touch like a desert to rain, betraying to him all the desperate need inside her.

There was a deliberate insolence in his caress that she knew was intended to humiliate her, but she could feel her breast swell with desire, the tender bud of her nipple hardening into his palm. She tried again weakly to struggle, but he held her down, demonstrating with devastating clarity that she was subject to his will, and would not escape until he was ready to let her go. His tongue was plundering all the sweetest depths of her mouth in a ruthless invasion, his caressing hand asserting a possessive claim over the ripe curves of her body, as if to warn her that this was the price he was exacting for the past week of his imprisonment.

It was only when she had finally ceased all attempts at resistance that he released her. She was dragging raggedly for breath, her face flushed and her clothes and hair dishevelled, but he seemed as ice-cool as ever—he wasn't even breathing any faster than usual.

She eyed him warily as she slid off the bed, resenting that he should be so little affected by what had been for her a devastating experience. The glint of mocking humour in his eyes as he watched her tug down her thick jumper seemed to warn her that even if she wore a suit of armoured steel she couldn't protect herself from him—he would always know how she looked, how she felt, beneath.

He rose easily to his feet, and picked up the elegant dinner-jacket which had been folded over the end of the bed. 'Well, now, since you've put me to so much inconvenience already, I really think the least you can do is drive me home, don't you? You do have a car,' he added, a sardonic inflexion in his voice. 'I noticed it the night you turned up at my house.'

'Oh . . . Yes, of course.' She might have known he would give her no chance to make an excuse. She eyed him in nervous apprehension as he casually shrugged his wide shoulders into his jacket, her mouth dry with an uncomfortable awareness of the contained power in that lean, muscular body.

The last thing she wanted to do was prolong this agony by driving him all the way back to London, but she knew it was useless to protest—he wanted her to do it, and he always got his own way. 'I . . . I'll just have to . . . pop upstairs and get my keys and things. I . . . won't be a minute.'

'Good. And bring that report of yours along, too. I'm interested to see what you have to say,' he added coolly as she stared up at him in blank amazement.

'But . . .'

'Why did I refuse to read it before?' he enquired, shrewdly guessing her question. 'I told you—I don't do anything under coercion. If you had simply done as I suggested, and sent it to my secretary, it would certainly have received the proper attention.'

'But we'd already sent it to you,' she protested bitterly. 'It came back with a terse letter stating that you had your own scientific experts. At least it got that much response—you just ignored our petition, and that had over five thousand signatures on it.'

He lifted one dark winged eyebrow in genuine surprise. 'Indeed? It appears that someone within my company has somewhat misguidedly taken it upon themselves to censor the information I receive.' His frown boded ill for that individual when he had discovered their identity. 'I can only apologise that you met with such an impolite response.'

'You mean you never even knew?' she questioned in disbelief. 'None of this was neccessary?' She laughed weakly, the whole of the past week suddenly taking on the characteristics of a very bad farce. 'Why didn't you tell us?'

'Initially, because I thought I was dealing with fanatics,' he responded drily. 'After that... Well, let us just say that I had my reasons.'

She slanted him a puzzled look, but she knew him well enough by now not to bother wasting her breath by asking what those reasons were. 'Oh, well.' She managed a small shrug, a gesture of wry resignation. 'I suppose it's too late to apologise now.'

'If by apologising you hope to escape the consequences,' he concurred without sympathy.

'I know.' She hung her head. 'I'm not looking forward to going to prison, but I suppose it's only what we deserve.'

'Quite.' And, casting one last look of distaste around the tiny cell, he walked out.

CHAPTER FOUR

IT WAS chilly outside after the cloying warmth of that
basement room. Andrea's elderly Beetle was parked
quite close to the building, and she unlocked the passenger door, slanting E.J. an awkward smile. 'I'm
afraid it's not quite the kind of car you're used to,'
she apologised.

'I'll manage,' he responded drily, easing his length
into the worn vinyl seat.

She went round to the driver's side, and slid herself
in behind the wheel, uncomfortably aware of his
closeness in the small car. 'Come on, Horace,' she
whispered to the temperamental engine as she turned
the ignition. 'Don't let me down.' It grumbled a bit,
but started. She slid it into gear, and pulled away.

He cast her a look of quizzical amusement. 'Why
do you call it Horace?'

A tinge of pink coloured her cheeks—she hadn't
meant him to hear that. 'It's because of the number-
plate,' she explained. 'HRS—Horace.'

'I see.' He nodded sagely, his glance taking in the
scruffy interior—there was a cardboard box full of
computer print-outs on the back seat, an old sweater
and a couple of empty carrier-bags on the floor, and
the door-pockets were stuffed with sweet-wrappings
and old petrol vouchers.

'I'm sorry,' she apologised, embarrassed by the
amount of junk. 'I keep meaning to clear it out.'

'Why bother?' His voice was laced with dry amusement. 'I'm sure all of it could be recycled in one way or another.'

She flickered him a wary look from beneath her lashes. That sardonic sense of humour had come as a surprise to her the first time he had allowed her to glimpse it. It was one of the things she liked most about him... *No*, she warned herself quickly; it would be far too dangerous to let herself begin to like him— it was quite bad enough that she had allowed herself to fall victim to his magnetic physical attraction.

They didn't talk much on the journey back to London. E.J. was reading her report, making rapid annotations in the margins with a slim gold pen. From time to time he asked her a question, and Andrea was impressed by his swift grasp of its contents.

The traffic on the motorway was heavy, and she began to worry that someone might recognise him from his picture, which had been constantly in the papers. But apparently no one was thinking of looking for a missing millionaire in a battered old Beetle stuck in a traffic jam on the M25, and they arrived at their destination without incident.

But as they turned into the elegant, tree-lined avenue, she was horrified to see a police car parked on the drive of his house, and a small cluster of what she guessed at once were journalists gathered around the wrought-iron gates.

'Drive past,' E.J. instructed briefly. 'Take the next left—we can get in the back way. I don't want to have to deal with any hassles with the Press until I'm ready.'

She obeyed, feeling a mixture of relief and apprehension. Sooner or later the police were going to have

to be told what had happened, and she was going to
have to face the consequences. But any postponement
of that moment was more than welcome.

He directed her into a narrower side-street, out of
sight of the watchers at the front. 'Park the car here,'
he instructed.

She slanted him a swift glance from beneath her
lashes. He seemed to have decided that she was going
to go into the house with him; she would really have
preferred not to, but even less did she want to get into
an argument that she was quite sure she would lose.
So she slid Horace into the place he had indicated,
and turned off the engine.

'Oh . . . I'm sorry—I'll have to let you out from the
outside,' she explained as he searched in vain for the
door-handle. 'The catch on the inside's broken.' She
scrambled out, and hurried round to open the door
for him, muttering curses to herself. He was going to
have her written off as a complete crank, she reflected
wryly, driving a decrepit old car like this, giving it a
name and talking to it—it hardly gave the impression
of a competent person whose scientific report deserved to be taken seriously.

They were outside the gates of a large building—it
looked as if it could be a private school or nursing
home of some kind. 'This way,' E.J. announced,
leading her into the grounds. 'I frequently use this
route when I want to avoid unwelcome attention.'

There was a high hedge and a wooden fence separ-
ating the grounds of the building from the gardens
of the houses beyond, but at a point he obviously
knew well E.J. lifted a branch, and showed her a
narrow, almost invisible path through the tangle of

undergrowth. They followed the path along the fence for a short distance, until they came to a place where a few of the planks were loose.

'Isn't this a little unsafe?' Andrea enquired as she climbed through into the back garden of his home. 'Aren't you afraid someone else might find this way in, and burgle you or something?'

He shrugged his wide shoulders in casual indifference. 'It wouldn't bother me if anyone stole my possessions.'

She slanted him a jaundiced glance from beneath her lashes. It must be nice to have so much wealth that you didn't have to care about anything being stolen—no doubt he could simply replace the contents of the whole house without even denting his petty cash.

The garden at the back of the house was as beautifully tended as that at the front. E.J. led her around the side, carefully keeping out of sight of the house, and, taking a key from his pocket, opened a door next to the garage. Standing aside, he gestured to her to precede him up the narrow stairs.

'I only use the rest of the house for business purposes,' he explained. 'I prefer to keep this apartment for my own use.'

She hesitated, reluctant to step inside, but drawn by a curiosity to see how he lived. And besides, she knew that she was going to have to face the inevitable sooner or later; once he informed the police that he was back, they would arrest her—it might as well be here as back at the university.

At the top of the stairs he opened another door—and she caught her breath in surprise; it was nothing

like how she had imagined it would be. The room was
large, and almost bare. The floor was of pale, polished wood, and the walls were washed white over
plain brick. There was a low wooden table in the
middle of the room, surrounded by half a dozen flat
cushions, and the only ornamentation was a simple
arrangement of twisted twigs in one corner, surrounded by a few smooth, polished stones.

'Oh . . . !'

He smiled, faintly amused at her astonishment.
'Make yourself comfortable,' he invited cordially. 'I'll
be with you as soon as I've taken a shower and prepared something to eat.'

She nodded dumbly, gazing around her. There was
something strangely restful about the austere purity
of the room, and after a while she decided that she
liked it—though she doubted that she could keep a
place so impressively free of junk.

It gave her quite a startling insight into the mind
of the man who lived here. She had already recognised his formidable intelligence and mental power,
and now she could see that his cool self-control went
very deep; his whole lifestyle reflected it. And they
had thought they could get the better of him, she reflected wryly. They had never stood a chance!

After a while she heard him in the kitchen, and
with some trepidation went in search of him. The
kitchen, too, was a masterpiece of austerity—sleek and
white, surgically clean—no toast crumbs lurking in
corners of the floor or forgotten coffee-cups quietly
festering on the window-sill here!

E.J. was dicing vegetables at the gleaming work-
station in the centre of the room. His hair was still

wet from his shower, and he was wearing a plain black
kimono-type robe that seemed to emphasise the
powerful breadth of his shoulders, the long, lean
muscularity of his frame. His feet were bare, and an
odd little *frisson* of heat shivered through her as she
realised that he was probably naked underneath the
robe. Her mouth felt suddenly dry; this was a man
whose body was as finely tuned as his mind. What
would it be like to make love with him . . . ?

He glanced over his shoulder, a cool glint of
amusement in his eyes as he recognised the hectic
thoughts in hers. 'Would you care for something to
eat?' he enquired, the polite host.

'Oh . . . Yes, thank you.' She wasn't really hungry,
but she had come to think of everything he said as
an order; besides, once the police came to arrest her
she didn't know when she might get her next decent
meal.

It was fascinating to watch him cooking; he worked
with an economy of movement, wielding the sharp
knife at a speed that would surely have taken his finger
off if he had made the slightest error. 'What are you
making?' she enquired, unable to supress her curiosity.

'*Hiya Yakko*—it's a Japanese dish. Vegetarian,' he
added, his sardonic smile emphasising the point.

'You're vegetarian?' She shook her head, laughing
in wry resignation. 'No wonder all those ridiculously
expensive steaks couldn't tempt you. Why didn't you
tell us?'

'Your efforts were a source of considerable
amusement,' he responded, those blue eyes glinting
with mocking humour. 'Besides, an occasional fast is

an excellent way of cleansing the body and concentrating the mind.'

She eyed him doubtfully; she couldn't imagine going without food for one day, let alone a whole week. 'Don't you get hungry?' she asked.

'Of course. But there's a great deal to be gained from cultivating the mental discipline to control one's physical appetites.' He slanted her a single meaningful look. 'It's only when you are able to restrain them at will that you can come to a complete realisation of all the pleasures in indulging them.'

She felt her heart thud, and wild blush colour her cheeks as his words conjured a swirl of fevered images. She had already experienced a little of the pleasure he was talking about—any more of it could drive her over the brink of insanity!

He had turned back to the preparation of the meal, arranging the trimmed vegetables into two delicately painted bowls, and adding a tiny bowl of soy sauce and another of horseradish sauce, setting them all out on a round tray. Then he took the pan of tofu that had been simmering on the hot-plate, and strained it swiftly into a bowl of iced water.

She watched him, intrigued by the attention to presentation and detail that transformed the simple food into a work of art. Inevitably her thoughts slid sideways again, and she found herself wondering... Sex as an art-form...? Now that was a thought to heat the blood...

'Are you ready to eat?'

She nodded, struggling to steady the uneven beating of her heart. He had picked up the tray, and was indicating to her to precede him back into the main room. He set the food down on the table, and sat down cross-legged on one of the cushions. Rather awkwardly, she sat down opposite him.

'Do you know how to use chopsticks?' he asked.

'Yes ... Well, sort of,' she amended, wryly aware that her technique would probably appear clumsy and slow to him.

'You should find these a little easier to use than the Chinese type,' he suggested, passing her a pair of short square sticks of polished wood.

'Oh ... Thank you.' She took them from him awkwardly; her fingers felt numb, and her hands were shaking slightly. She tried to take up a piece of tofu from the bowl, but it refused to co-operate. 'Rats!' she muttered, struggling to pick it up again.

He laughed softly, reaching across the table to take both her hands in his. 'You really have a problem with those shaking hands, don't you, Carrots?' he taunted, smiling into her eyes with a mockery that told her that he was quite well aware of the real cause of her clumsiness. 'Here, this is the way to do it.'

His touch was firm and sure, moving her fingers into the correct position. But she couldn't concentrate on her hands; lowering her eyes from his face, she had found herself focusing instead on the deep V of his chest in the wrap of his kimono. His skin gleamed a healthy light bronze from the sun, and there was just enough of a scattering of rough, dark, curling hair at the base of his throat for her to imagine running her fingers through it. Suddenly it was hard to breathe.

'Is that better?'

'Oh... Yes... Thank you...' This was getting really crazy; she had never reacted like this to a man before—she hadn't believed she was capable of it! But this one exuded a kind of raw sensuality that she didn't know how to deal with. Desperately her mind sought for some safe topic of conversation. 'By the way, what did you... think of the report?' she managed.

He accepted the subject with only a faint quirk of sardonic humour. 'Very thorough,' he accorded. 'I was surprised at some of your figures—oh, I don't doubt them,' he added as she opened her mouth to protest. 'I'm sure you took great pains to be accurate, knowing that I could have my own scientists recheck them—and possibly sue you for libel if they were incorrect.'

The glint in his eyes warned her that he was serious, and she blinked at him in shock—he really did play rough! But she returned his gaze defiantly. 'So, now that you've read it, are you going to do anything about it?' she demanded, a good deal more forcefully than she felt.

'I already had.' He took a small piece of diced vegetable neatly with his chopsticks and dipped it into the soy sauce, and slipped it into his mouth. 'That part of the production process has been shut down until a complete review has been undertaken. We'll be acquiring new equipment for the plant, and instigating new procedures. And the management responsible is being replaced.'

She realised that she was staring at him with her mouth open, and shut it quickly. 'But... that'll cost millions!' she protested.

He lifted one dark eyebrow in quizzical enquiry. 'Isn't that what you wanted?'

'Well... Yes, of course—it's even more than we wanted. But... Why didn't you tell us all that right away? We wouldn't have... We would have let you go at once.'

That disturbingly sensual mouth curled into a smile. 'As I explained to you at the time, it goes against all my inclinations to negotiate under duress,' he responded, a hard edge of steel in his voice.

'But I told you why we had to do that,' she argued, her eyes sparking. 'We didn't seem to be getting our message across any other way.'

'I have some sympathy with your aims,' he acknowledged. 'Though I can't say I approve of your methods.'

She was forced to concede on that point. 'I know. I...I'm sorry.' It seemed totally inadequate, but what else could she say? 'We must have caused you...quite a lot of inconvenience.'

'That's something of an understatement,' he responded drily. 'I'm due to go to Japan on very important business the day after tomorrow, and this incident has considerably disrupted my preparations.'

'I'm...sorry.' She hung her head. 'I suppose...you'd better call the police now, and get it over with.' The tension of waiting for the sword to fall was telling on her nerves—she was beginning to suspect that he was deliberately delaying the moment simply to torment her. 'We don't want to waste any more of their time.'

'In a few moments.' He was regarding her with a level gaze, those blue eyes totally unreadable. 'Have you ever been to Japan?' he enquired.

'Japan?' She shook her head, puzzled by the question. 'No.'

'It's a very beautiful country—especially at this time of year, when the cherry-blossom is just coming into flower. Parts of it are almost tropical, and yet there are ice-floes off the coast of the northern islands in winter.'

She was still staring at him blankly, confused by these reflections.

'I've been doing business there for a number of years,' he went on, apparently quite inconsequentially. 'It can be quite a challenge—their methods and traditions are very different from ours. This particular trip will be the culmination of something I've been working on for the past eighteen months. I want you to come with me.'

A surge of heat flooded through her. '*What*?'

'I want you to come to Japan with me,' he repeated, his voice cool and even. 'For one week. A week of your life, in exchange for the week that you stole of mine. There's a certain poetic justice in that, don't you think?'

Her mind was in a spin. He surely couldn't mean...? No—in spite of those couple of kisses, she wasn't deluded into believing that he was suffering from any wild passion for her. And besides, he wasn't the kind of man who would need to make those sort of bargains to get a woman into bed. 'I...I don't think I quite understand...' she stammered.

He took another piece of diced vegetable very precisely with his chopsticks. 'As I said, it can be quite a challenge doing business with the Japanese. Mr Tsutsumi, the head of the corporation I have been negotiating with, has kept me waiting for far longer than I would have liked to conclude this deal—thus giving himself an advantage, in that by the very fact that I held on I have betrayed how keen I am on it. Now he is ready to sign—and it's my turn to play a little game.'

'But...where do I fit in?' she queried, still confused.

'You are a representative from an environmental agency that has been causing me a considerable nuisance,' he responded without a trace of irony. 'You are already threatening to delay the building of the factory Tsutsumi and I will be building in this country, by challenging the planning application on the grounds that it will cause pollution. The only way I can satisfy you is by taking you along to see for yourself the production process. You'll ask lots of awkward questions, and find something to object to—something fairly minor...'

'What if I can't find anything?'

His smile was bland. 'I'm quite confident that you'll be able to unearth *something*,' he responded with dry humour. 'Thus you'll provide me with an excuse to appear to be wavering at the last minute—though not so much that I'll want to pull out of the deal altogether.'

'And what do I get out of it?' she demanded edgily.

'You said that you weren't looking forward to going to prison,' he reminded her with a bland smile. 'Do as I ask, and it won't be necessary.'

She raised one eyebrow in frank scepticism. 'And how will you arrange that?' she enquired.

He lifted his wide shoulders in a negligent shrug. 'It's entirely up to me how much I choose to tell the police about the past week,' he pointed out. 'If I decide not to give them any clues, it's extremely unlikely that they'll link you to my disappearance, let alone turn up any evidence.'

'I see.' Her jaw was rigid with tension. She could only marvel at the subtlety of his strategy. When had he knitted this particular scheme together? It was quite a masterpiece of manipulation, offering her such a beguiling alternative to a prospect she dreaded. But she knew she had to refuse—the deeper she allowed herself to be drawn into his coils, the more dangerous it would be. She shook her head firmly. 'No. I'm sorry—I can't come to Japan with you.'

His eyes remained coolly enigmatic. 'You'd rather go to prison after all?'

'No, of course not! But...' She *mustn't* let herself be tempted—she was quite sure that what appeared to be the easiest option would turn out to be very far from that.

He continued to eat his meal, giving all the appearance of total indifference to her decision. 'Well, it's your choice, of course,' he conceded smoothly. 'I dare say you'd probably only get about five years, so you could be out in ... what, two, if you were lucky? It's a pity about your career, though—with a criminal record, I doubt if any university would consider employing you again.'

She returned him an icy glare. He was absolutely right, of course—her career would be in ruins.

'Still, I suppose you could always fall back on teaching,' he went on, assuming an air of detached interest. 'Of course, you'd be likely to encounter the same problem, but I dare say some of the inner-city schools would be so desperate that they might be prepared to take you on.'

She closed her eyes briefly, wishing she could shut out that soft, insidious voice as he unerringly sketched out one of her worst nightmares; some of her friends had gone into teaching after graduation, and she didn't envy them, standing up every day in front of a class of unruly teenagers who weren't remotely interested in learning anything about science. But she mustn't let that sway her judgement...

'And then, of course, there's your young friends,' he went on, twisting the knife of guilt. 'Some people might think that, as their tutor, you had some sort of responsibility towards them, having led them into such a risky course of action. But perhaps you wouldn't agree?'

She opened her eyes again to glare at him in cold fury. 'Of course I feel a responsibility for them,' she protested, torn by the dilemma he was deliberately confronting her with. 'But...'

'And even if you don't feel any concern for your students, I'm sure you must for your parents.' His voice was treacherously smooth. 'Didn't you say your father had been ill?'

She felt an icy chill wrap around her heart. She had known he must have had some kind of ulterior motive for his apparent interest in her family; had he been planning even then to use them to coerce her into doing what he wanted?

And she knew she had no choice. With deadly accuracy he had identified her most vulnerable spot. Her parents would be horrified if she was arrested on such a serious charge as kidnapping, with all the attendant publicity. She couldn't put them through that.

'But as you say, we don't want to waste any more police time,' he added mockingly. He began to rise to his feet, but it was only a token gesture. He knew he had her exactly where he wanted her.

'No.' She hung her head, her voice a ragged whisper. 'All right—I'll go with you.'

'Good.' He accepted her acquiescence with cool satisfaction. 'I thought you would be intelligent enough to see the wisdom of my proposal. Now, my chauffeur will collect you at nine-thirty tomorrow morning, and will take you to a salon, where you will have your hair cut...'

'Have my hair cut?' she protested, bewildered. 'But why?'

'If you're going to be travelling with me, I'd prefer that you look presentable,' he responded drily. 'Then you'll be taken to select some suitable clothes...'

'I've got plenty of clothes.'

'If what I've seen you wearing to date is anything to go by, the best place for them is the dustbin. Dalton will take you to the shops you are to use, and they will know the kind of thing I wish you to have—the accounts will be sent to me. Do you have any questions?'

'Wh-what am I going to tell everyone?' she asked unsteadily. 'I can't just disappear for a whole week without some kind of explanation.'

'I leave that to your inventive mind,' he responded, an inflexion of sardonic humour in his voice. 'Dalton will come for you on Thursday afternoon to bring you to the airport. Any other problems?'

'N-no.' A different kind of chill was curling around her heart; the ruthless efficiency with which he had handed out her instructions was almost frightening. But why should he be so concerned about the way she looked? Unless ... Unless he *was* expecting that part of the deal would be that she should sleep with him as well.

But what could she do? The alternative was to put her parents through an ordeal that could very easily kill her father. And then there were her students; there was no doubt that it *was* her fault they had got themselves into this—they were young and impressionable, and as their tutor they looked up to her. If she had argued more strongly against Brian's crazy scheme from the beginning, they would never have gone through with it.

And after all, she reasoned rationally, it would only be for a week ... And you *know* you want to go with him, a voice inside her head taunted. She tried to deny it, but she knew that it was true—from the first moment she had seen him, she had felt that powerful physical attraction that was becoming almost an obsession.

Of course, she knew that he was offering her nothing more than one single week of shallow carnal pleasure—but at least she could have that one week of being close to him, one week of those long, slow, deep kisses, those magical caresses ...

She caught herself up sharply, her cheeks hot and her heart pounding. She didn't even know if that *was* what he was intending—and, even if it was, she didn't have to go along with it. In spite of everything, she still had the option of refusing. He was hardly likely to force her, for goodness' sake—he wasn't a barbarian! But the trouble was, she acknowledged wryly, that he was unlikely to need to resort to force—not when he had such effective powers of persuasion.

He was watching her, those cool blue eyes far too perceptive, reading all the thoughts that were passing through her brain. 'Do we have a deal?' he enquired. She drew a long, steadying breath, and nodded her head. 'Y—yes.'

At least this way she would be the only one to bear the burden—her parents need never even know about it. And once it was all over, she would never have to see him again; she could go back to her normal life as if nothing had happened, instead of having to face the long-drawn-out nightmare of waiting to go to trial, and then prison.

Just one week. Surely that had to be the lesser of the two evils—didn't it?

CHAPTER FIVE

ANDREA had travelled from Heathrow Airport on several occasions, but she had never been driven up to the doors in a chauffeur-driven Rolls-Royce before, nor had a polite porter convey an extremely smart Louis Vuitton suitcase bearing her name to the first-class check-in counter.

Yesterday had been quite a day. If Dalton, the chauffeur, had recognised her from the night he had thrown her off E.J.'s drive, he was far too well-schooled to show any sign of it; and if he thought his instructions for the day at all unusual, he hadn't betrayed it by so much as a flicker.

He had driven her first to a very exclusive Knightsbridge beauty salon, where she was evidently expected. Her first glance around the place had terrified her—she always found hairdressers intimidating, and preferred to let one of her sisters trim her hair when it needed it. This place, with its plush carpets and white Italian furniture, was the stuff of her nightmares.

But in fact the stylist had been very reassuring. He had suggested taking just a few inches off the length of her hair, and thinning it out a little so that it would be easier to manage. Bearing in mind E.J.'s dictates, she had fatalistically agreed to whatever the stylist suggested, but she had to admit that the result was a considerable improvement.

Feeling a little self-conscious with her new look, she had been whisked off to the kind of elegant designer boutique that she would never have dreamed of entering in normal circumstances. Apparently E.J. had found time in his schedule to issue orders to the chic young woman who managed the place, and she had found herself being whisked in and out of the changing-room, trying on suits and dresses and smart casual-wear—none of them with a price tag. Then had come the accessories—shoes, handbags, scarves, jewellery... and underwear.

The thought of that underwear made her blush. Oh, it was beautiful; dainty wisps of silk and lace, in every delicate shade under the sun—the sort of stuff she would never have bought for herself in a million years. And nightgowns, floating and sensuous, a different one for each night.

Their purchase had seemed to confirm the uneasy suspicions that had been plaguing her since this trip had first been mentioned—E.J. was assuming that she was going to be willing to sleep with him, as part of the price of his silence to the police. Though quite why he should go to such elaborate lengths to seduce her she wasn't sure—he must know that she would in all probability have succumbed with no more temptation than a few of those devastating kisses.

And what of that complicated story about Mr Tsutsumi? Had that just been a blind? Or was there still more to all this than she had yet worked out?

Anyway, here she was, waiting in the unfamiliar luxury of the first-class lounge for E.J. to arrive. She felt like a stranger to herself in the expensive blue silk suit she was wearing; it was beautifully cut to flatter her slender figure, with a classically styled jacket with deep lapels and a slight flare over her hips, and a pencil-slim skirt a fashionable inch or two above her knees.

And unlike most men she had known, E.J. apparently wasn't troubled by her height—it had been made quite clear that the only shoes she was to choose from were those with the kind of slim high heels she had always wanted to wear but had avoided out of a reluctance to tower over everyone around her. But even now, she wouldn't tower over him, she reflected, a small shimmer of heat running through her. He was more than a match for her.

A swift glance at her watch—one of the few things of her own she was being allowed to retain—told her that it must be nearly time for their flight to be called, and she glanced around, wondering where E.J. could be. At that moment he swung in briskly through the frosted-glass doors, instantly striking in an immaculate dark grey business suit, a slim briefcase in his hand.

She rose unsteadily to her feet, her mouth dry, her heart pounding. The force of her own reaction alarmed her—there was no need to be quite such a willing victim, for goodness' sake! She drew in a long, deep breath, struggling to compose herself.

He acknowledged the greeting of the ground-steward, who obviously knew him extremely well, and crossed the room towards her. She felt her cheeks grow warm under the appraising scrutiny of those cool blue eyes, conscious that everything she was wearing, from the skin out, had been bought by him.

He completed his assessment, his eyes registering a faintly quizzical approval. 'Very nice,' he accorded, a note of satisfaction in his tone. 'Have you been waiting long? I think there's time for us to have one drink before our flight is called.'

'Thank you.' With an effort of will, she held her head high as she sat down opposite him. She felt like a piece of property, decked out according to his exact specifications; and for one week that was exactly what she was, she acknowledged with a taut little twist of humiliation. No longer her own person, every aspect of her appearance and behaviour subject to his control.

E.J. had summoned the ground-steward, and slanted Andrea an enquiring glance. 'What will you have?'

'Oh... A... dry Martini, please,' she managed a little awkwardly—she wasn't accustomed to all this first-class service. The steward nodded, and went to fetch her order, and Andrea slanted E.J. an acid look. 'I *am* still allowed to choose what I'll eat and drink, then?' she challenged, an edge in her voice.

'Of course,' He seemed quite untroubled by her poison dart.

'Well, that's reassuring.' It was maddeningly impossible to have a good quarrel with such a master of sang-froid.

He lounged back in the comfortable armchair, regarding her in amused enquiry. 'You don't like the clothes?'

'Oh, they're very nice—though not exactly what I would have chosen for myself.'

'Of course not,' he responded, a sarcastic inflexion in his tone. 'But your own taste, if you will forgive me for saying so, had definite room for improvement.'

'I didn't want it improved,' she countered tartly. 'Least of all by you.'

'But you have to admit I've made a good job of it,' he pointed out with incontrovertible logic. 'You look very elegant.'

She slanted him a look of angry resentment. 'Do you make a habit of rearranging people like this?'

'Not people, usually,' he acknowledged. 'Companies. I take over ones that appear to have potential, often potential that they haven't even recognised themselves, and impose my own style of management to bring them around.'

'I'm not a company,' she retorted icily.

'I'm quite well aware of that.' His tone was one of calm patience, almost as if he were speaking to a rebellious child. 'And I haven't taken you over—at least, only temporarily. On our return from Japan, you'll be free to return to your horrific sweaters and your frumpy shoes...'

'Frumpy...!'

His eyes glinted in mocking amusement. 'Weren't they?' he challenged.

She hesitated, furious with him, but too honest to deny it. 'Heels usually make me too tall,' she defended weakly.

'You should be proud of your height—a lot of models would envy you your looks.' His words startled her into silence, and he laughed drily. 'Don't you believe me? I told you, I never say things simply for the pleasure of hearing myself speak. Doesn't your friend

Brian ever pay you any compliments? No, I don't suppose he would,' he answered himself with caustic humour. 'He's much too busy being a highly respected expert in his field.'

As usual, he was devastatingly accurate in his assessment, and she didn't know how to respond. But fortunately at that moment the ground-steward returned with her drink, and she was able to sit back, sipping the cool iced liquid and watching the planes taxiing across the apron outside and taking off into the high blue sky.

E.J. had opened his briefcase and taken out some papers, and she slanted him a covert glance from beneath her lashes. He seemed virtually to have forgotten her presence, and she couldn't help but envy him that ability to switch his attention at will, focusing totally on one thing to the apparent exclusion of all else. If she really *had* been his mistress, she would have resented it intensely; as it was, she knew she had no right to object.

It gave her a slightly odd feeling to realise that not a soul knew where she was; if the plane should crash, it would come as quite a surprise to everyone to find out that she'd been on her way to Japan with E.J. Preston! She hadn't liked to lie, but she hadn't cared to face the complications of explaining the truth, so for her parents she had invented an important conference in Glasgow that she had had the opportunity to attend at the last minute, while for everyone at the university, including Brian, she had similarly made up an urgent family crisis. She only hoped that they would all heed her pious pleas not to be contacted except in the most dire emergency—if one side spoke to the other, the cat would really be among the pigeons!

It was about ten minutes later that the steward came over to tell them that their flight was being called. In spite of all the circumstances, Andrea was aware of a little surge of excitement running through her as they made their way along the endless airport corridors to their departure gate—she loved flying, and Japan was a country she had always longed to visit, but had known she could never afford, unless she should ever be fortunate enough to be sent there by the university for a conference or something.

But a covert glance up at the rather forbidding man at her side reminded her that this was going to be no pleasure trip—he had brought her along for reasons of his own, and she still wasn't sure exactly what those reasons were.

She had often wondered, when she had been crowded into the narrow economy seats, what it was like up in that first-class world in the cabin above. Climbing the short spiral staircase, she found out. It was sheer luxury. The seats were wide and deep, with more than enough room for her long legs; a charming stewardess took her jacket to hang it up, and brought her champagne, ensuring that she was comfortable in her window-seat.

E.J. slanted her a glance of dry humour, correctly interpreting her thoughts. 'The facilities are a little better than those provided in any of Her Majesty's prisons, I would imagine,' he remarked in a quiet voice.

She conceded a reluctant smile. 'I expect they are.' She sipped her champagne, wryly reflecting that she

could still find that she had chosen the more
dangerous option. But it was too late to change her
mind now. 'How did you manage to put the police
off?' she enquired, keeping her tone light. 'They must
have needed some kind of explanation for your
disappearance.'

'I gave them to understand that I suspected it was
in connection with an important business deal, the
details of which I was unwilling to disclose. I'm afraid
they've come to the conclusion that I'm obstructive
and unhelpful, but there wasn't a great deal they could
do about it. They seemed to feel in the end that, as
I was the one who'd suffered, if I chose to be fool
enough to let the culprits get away with it it was my
own look-out.'

'Oh . . .' She could well imagine the scene; the un-
fortunate detective drafted on to the case wouldn't
have stood a chance.

He had opened his briefcase again, and she turned
to gaze out of the window as the plane began the long
taxi out to the runway for take-off. What *was* he going
to demand as the price for not handing her over to
the police? She still couldn't quite bring herself to believe that he really would expect her to sleep with him,
and yet . . .

If only he would tell her right out what his terms
were, instead of torturing her with this uncertainty.
But of course it was probably quite deliberate, she
mused bitterly—he had warned her that she would
have to pay for that week stolen out of his life, and
this could be his way of exacting a few extra ounces
of punishment.

And it shamed her to have to admit that she was half hoping that he really *did* intend that she should share his bed. She might curse herself for a fool, remind herself that when the week was over it was going to be even more difficult to piece together the broken shards of her heart, but it didn't help. At least she would have the memory of that one week, to hold on to for the rest of her life.

She stroked her hand over the smooth kid leather of her Gucci handbag, guiltily aware of the secret hidden inside. Somehow, in the midst of all the emotional turmoil of the past forty-eight hours, she had been rational enough to take the precaution of visiting the university clinic, and providing herself with the simplest protection against the possible consequences of this trip.

It had amazed her that she could be so cold-blooded about it, but perhaps it was just as well that part of her mind could retain some semblance of her usual sane common sense—it would have been all too easy to let herself slip into a foolish romantic fantasy, and that would have been to risk courting disaster.

Still pretending to be looking out of the window, she slanted a covert glance at the man at her side. He was studying those papers again, scanning them with rapid concentration, making notes in the margin as he had on the report she had written. He read very fast, but she knew how much detail he could take in— was that an innate skill, or something else he had trained himself to do?

He really was quite a formidable person, she reflected: mentally, physically, and emotionally. He seemed so much in control, both of himself and of everything around him. And of *everyone* around him, she added, an odd little shiver of heat scudding down her spine. He had manipulated her into a position where she had had no choice but to agree to his proposition, just as he was planning to use her to manipulate the situation in Japan to his own advantage. And whatever else he wanted ...

The sound of the engines grew suddenly louder, and with a powerful thrust the huge, ungainly aeroplane surged forward. Andrea held her breath in a moment of taut anticipation, watching the ground rush by; and then suddenly they lifted off, climbing at a steep angle above the houses and fields, the busy motorway falling away beneath them.

Like the bumble-bee, the 747 looked as if it should never be able to fly. But it did, smoothly and quietly—up here in the odd-looking bulge above the wings there was virtually no engine noise at all once they were airborne. The seatbelt light had barely gone out before the stewardess came to hand them the menu for dinner, and there was more champagne, as well as the chance to watch a soppy romantic film on the video screen beside her seat.

They had taken off a little after six o'clock, and now the sun was setting into the mists of the west in a blaze of scarlet and magenta. As night closed around them, there was a strange atmosphere of intimacy in the hushed cabin—there were only a few other passengers travelling first class besides themselves. It seemed to make Andrea all the more acutely aware of the man beside her, still intent on his papers. They would be confined here together for fifteen hours—all through the night. And it would be evening again by the time they arrived in Tokyo, with another night to come...

E.J. glanced across, a smile of amusement flickering in his eyes when he saw which film she was watching. 'Enjoying yourself, Carrots?' he enquired.

A swift tinge of pink coloured her cheeks. 'Yes, thank you,' she responded, her voice sounding slightly strained to her own ears. His adoption of that pet name for her—one she had endured agonies over when she was at school—had seemed just part of the barbed mockery he had tormented her with while he had been her prisoner. But now...it seemed to conjure up an illusion of closeness and affection, as if they had known each other for a very long time. It was becoming quite difficult to hold on to the reality of the situation—the mirages he was spinning were beginning to confuse her as much as they were designed to confuse everyone else.

She had been drifting for a while on the fringes of sleep when she became conscious of E.J. leaning over her. She caught her breath in alarm, flinching back into the corner of her seat. 'What...do you want? she demanded, instantly defensive.

One dark eyebrow lifted a fraction of an inch. 'I was simply reclining your seat for you,' he responded evenly. 'If you want to sleep, you'll be more comfortable.'

'Oh...thank you.' Her heartbeat was racing so fast that she found it difficult to breathe.

A glint of mocking amusement was lurking in the depths of those cool blue eyes. 'What did you think I wanted?' he enquired, taunting softly.

'I . . . I don't know.' She cast him a searching glance from beneath her lashes. 'I don't know what you want,' she whispered tautly.

He didn't answer her—he simply returned her one of those cool, enigmatic looks, inviting her to draw her own conclusions, and turned his attention back to his papers. Frustrated, she turned her shoulder against him, huddling down beneath the warm vicuña blanket the stewardess had brought her, holding herself as far away from him as she possibly could. Outside there was only darkness—there was no moon, and they were flying above a thick layer of cloud that hid everything below from sight; they could have been flying into outer space. The only sound was the faint, somnolent drone of the engines, and her own quiet breathing . . .

'Ladies and gentlemen, please fasten your seatbelts.'

Andrea gazed out of the window, entranced by her first glimpse of Japan—it seemed to be the most beautiful spot on earth. The sun was glinting on high, snow-covered alps, carved by deeply wooded valleys and tranquil lakes, and all around the Pacific Ocean was the deepest, purest blue.

A faint yellow haze hung over Tokyo Bay, but she could glimpse a little of the vast urban sprawl below as the huge plane banked and began to descend steeply into Narita airport, its shadow racing across the ground below until it touched down with just the slightest bump.

She heaved a sigh of relief. Even in the cosseted comfort of the first-class cabin, it had been a very long flight. Her neck ached slightly, and her skin felt

dry, and she was just plain tired of sitting down—
though when she stood up she found that her head
still felt slightly dizzy, as if the plane were still moving.

The first-class passengers were the first to dis-
embark, the stewardesses who had taken care of them
for the past fifteen hours bidding them a pleasant
goodbye. And then they were out on solid ground at
last, walking through the long airport corridors—so
similar in international airports throughout the world.
This was probably one of the busiest she had ever
seen, though, and she would have felt lost without
E.J. to follow—he seemed to know exactly where he
was going.

'Have you been here often before?' she asked him.

He nodded. 'Frequently.'

She slanted him a wry glance from beneath her
lashes. He looked as fresh as if he had flown from
London to Birmingham, not halfway round the world.
'Don't you even get jet-lag?' she enquired, faintly re-
sentful. 'No, I don't suppose you do—that's only for
lesser mortals.'

He laughed drily. 'I travel a great deal—you get
used to it.'

They had reached Immigration Control, and he
handed over his passport, exchanging a few words
with the officer behind the desk, who seemed at first
surprised and then pleased that a Westerner should
be able to speak his language so fluently.

They collected their baggage, and were through
Customs within minutes. Reaching the bustling ar-
rivals hall, E.J. glanced around, his height giving him
the advantage of being able to see over the heads of
the crowd. 'Ah!' He had seen whoever it was he was

looking for, and made a beeline for them, neatly forging a path through the throng for Andrea to follow in his wake.

A small deputation seemed to have arrived to meet them; five men, all uniformly dressed in smart and conservative dark suits, bowing and exchanging business cards with E.J. with a formal courtesy that fascinated Andrea—it was a reminder that, in spite of the superficial similarities, she was in a country with a very different history and culture.

She was briefly introduced, and found herself bowing too, not quite sure of the correct etiquette required but relieved to find that they were all smiling and more than ready to forgive her any mistakes. It was all going to take quite a lot of getting used to, she reflected, wishing she had had more time to read up about the country—all she had to guide her was a small tourist pocket-book she had bought at the airport.

The greetings accomplished, they set off towards the exit. Outside, Andrea was surprised to find not one but two long black limousines awaiting them. 'I've arranged for you to be taken directly to where we're staying,' E.J. informed her with all his usual high-handed directness. 'I expect you're tired.'

She looked up at him sharply. 'Well . . . Yes, I am,' she conceded, alarmed at the thought of being left alone in a very foreign country where she spoke not a word of the language. 'But...where are you going?'

'I have a meeting with Mr Tsutsumi,' he explained briskly. 'Don't worry, you'll be all right, I'm not leaving you to book into a strange hotel on your own—Mr Tsutsumi has invited us to stay as guests at his own home.'

She frowned, puzzled and a little suspicious. 'You never told me that.'

He lifted one dark eyebrow fractionally in surprise that she should question him over such an insignificant detail. 'Does it make any difference?' he enquired.

'Well... No, I suppose not,' she conceded uncertainly. 'In fact it'll probably be much nicer to stay with a real Japanese family.' But she had her reservations. For one thing, the thought of being the guest of total strangers for a whole week was a little nerve-racking. And for another... Why *hadn't* he told her? She was so mistrustful of him that even this seemed a deliberate act of manipulation on his part, yet another strategy in his clever games.

'Our hostess will make you very welcome,' he assured her. 'Here, take this for her.' He opened his briefcase, and took out a small, beautifully wrapped parcel. 'It's a tradition here for a guest to take a present—rather a nice tradition, I think. Off you go— I'll see you later.'

Thus dismissed, there was little she could do but obey his instructions once again. A polite chauffeur, the impassive Dalton's brother under the skin, was holding open the door, having placed both her and E.J.'s baggage in the back. Wryly reflecting that this was exactly how she had begun her journey, and that she was no wiser now than when she had set out about the prospects that lay in front of her, she climbed into the car and sat back on the comfortable leather seat.

At least it would be nice to reach her destination, wherever it was, and be able to relax and unwind a little. A nice warm bath, and somewhere to lie down for a while, somewhere cool and quiet—that was what she needed.

CHAPTER SIX

A KALEIDOSCOPE of images was spinning in Andrea's tired brain. It had been a much longer journey than she had expected from the airport, much of it on a busy expressway that circled Tokyo Bay. She had been able to see little but the giant industrial installations around the harbour, and a few hazy glimpses of the vast concrete and steel metropolis beyond.

But now they had left the twenty-first century behind, and seemed to have travelled back in time to an older Japan; they were driving through a district of wooded hillsides and quiet houses screened by tall bamboo fences, and here and there through the trees she could catch glimpses of the deep blue Pacific.

The eight-hour time-difference meant that already it was darkening to evening again; it was odd to think that at home it was still eleven o'clock in the morning—that time-difference added to the confusing sense of disorientation she was feeling.

At long last the car drew to a halt beside a long fence. Night had fallen now, and through the gaps in the bamboo slats Andrea could glimpse lights. As she gazed in fascination, trying to see more, the chauffeur came and opened the door for her, bowing politely as she alighted. A gate was opened, and she found herself walking into a dream.

The house was long and low, built of wood—dark, like mahogany—with a gracefully tapered roof of grey

tiles. A wide veranda ran all the way round it, and
the lights within were softly filtered by white paper
screens. It stood in a lovely garden, shaded by a few
delicate trees and shrubs, with a ground of pale gravel
combed into fluid lines around just one or two carefully chosen moss-covered rocks.

But the illusion that she had somehow wandered
on to a stage set for a performance of *Madama
Butterfly* was quickly shattered when a slim young
woman in blue denim jeans and a vividly patterned
red shirt, her sleek blue-black hair bouncing in a
ponytail on the back of her head, erupted from the
house in a swirl of loud pop music, and skipped down
to meet her, her hands outstretched in welcome.

'Hi—you're Andrea! Did you have a good journey?
You must be bushed!' The snappy American accent
switched off abruptly as she addressed an imperious
instruction to the chauffeur, then she turned back to
Andrea again. 'I've told him to take your bags straight
to your room,' she explained. 'Come on inside—I bet
you could use a coffee?'

'Thank you.' Slightly bemused, Andrea allowed
herself to be led up the stone path to the house.

In the small entrance-hall, her hostess paused briefly
to kick off her shoes, leaving them lying side by side
on the floor; Andrea hesitated, unsure once again of
the required form—was she supposed to take her shoes
off too? If only E.J. were here to tell her what to do!
Uncertainly, she copied the Japanese girl, and won a
beaming smile of approval.

'Here are some slippers for you—I hope they'll be
big enough.'

Since the girl was tiny, with dainty little feet, Andrea could readily aquit her of intending any slight—her own size sevens must seem enormous to her. She tucked her feet into the slippers, and stepped up into the house.

The traditional styling of the outside was continued in the interior—pale tatami matting scattered with low cushions covered the wooden floors, and the walls were white paper screens. Apart from the cushions, the main item of furniture was a laquered table. On the wall behind it there was a scroll, depicting a graceful black and white crane perched on a twisted branch, against a background of a snow-capped mountain, perfectly complemented by the delicate arrangement of day-lilies and bare twigs in a glass vase.

She couldn't see where the music was coming from—the equipment, and the speakers, were concealed out of sight. It would have been very much to E.J.'s taste, she reflected, recalling the similarity of his own apartment, though he had captured the essence of the style rather than actually copying it.

A young Filipina girl, wearing a rather faded cotton dress, came into the room, and Miss Ponytail spoke to her briskly, sending her scurrying away. 'Come and sit down,' she invited Andrea brightly, kicking off her slippers before crossing the tatami. 'Are you into this kind of music? I think this band is just amazing!'

Andrea again copied her hostess, accepting the offer of a seat, though she found the unfamiliar low cushion a little uncomfortable. She was still struggling to cope with all these bewildering impressions. Contrasts and contradictions were crowding in on her, confusing her—the timeless Oriental tranquillity of the house, disrupted by the noisy Western music, her hostess with her almost too exuberant friendliness and her high-handed manner towards the servants. She needed time to take it all in, but instead she was having to struggle to respond politely to the Japanese girl's flow of artless chatter.

'Is this your first trip to Japan? We're most honoured by your visit. I've never been to England, but I've been to the States—have you ever been there? I just love L.A.—the shops are just amazing. I hope you'll be able to come and see the shops in Tokyo while you're here—you can buy just about anything you want. I'd just love to show you around.'

'I... That would be nice,' Andrea managed weakly. Remembering the gift E.J. had given her for their hostess, she opened her bag and took it out. 'This is...for you,' she offered with a stiff smile. 'From...E.J.'

'Oh... How kind of him.'

Rather to her surprise, the pretty parcel was accepted with an air of casual indifference, and set down on a low laquered table against the wall, unopened. Confused and embarrassed, afraid that she had inadvertently commited some serious breach of etiquette, she turned her resentment against E.J.—he ought to be here, not leaving her to cope on her own.

'Where is Edward, anyway?' the other girl enquired languidly. 'Gone off to some dull old business meeting with my father, I suppose?'

'Er—yes.' So she was Mr Tsutsumi's daughter, then? At least that answered one question, Andrea reflected wryly. At first sight, she had assumed the girl was a teenager, but having studied her a little more closely she had concluded that she was rather older—she had even wondered if she might be Mr Tsutsumi's wife.

But she was still a little uncertain what to make of her. There was something...less than straight-forward about her. Maybe it was her eyes—they seemed too wide and round for that classically Japanese face, as if she had had them altered by plastic surgery to conform to some incongruous notion of beauty. Or maybe it was the way she had spoken of E.J.—or rather Edward, as she had called him. There had been a little too much studied disinterest in her tone, as if she was trying to hide something.

A whole new scenario now seemed to present itself. Could the reason for E.J. bringing her with him have something to do with this pretty Japanese girl? Was there something between them? Maybe Mr Tsutsumi wouldn't approve of his daughter having an affair with a foreigner, and she was here to quiet his suspicions while the contract was signed...?

But her brain was really too tired to think about it at the moment—no doubt she would find out soon enough what was going on. The maid had come back, bringing coffee, and she took a cup with a murmur of thanks.

'I would have given you tea,' twittered the other girl brightly, dismissing the servant with a casual wave of her hand. 'But *geijin* don't like it much to drink. Though of course I expect you'll want to see a tea ceremony while you're here. And the Kabuki theatre—you'd find the Noh plays much too difficult to understand.'

Again Andrea felt that odd clash of impressions that she couldn't quite put her finger on. The girl was speaking pleasantly enough, but she had clearly categorised her as an ignorant tourist, incapable of appreciating the subtlety of Japanese taste. She found herself resenting that.

'By the way, I'm sorry but I . . . didn't catch your name?' she enquired, a little embarrassed at having to ask.

The girl laughed archly. 'Didn't Edward tell you? Oh, that's too bad of him! I shall have to give him a real good scold when I see him.' But the glint in her eyes promised something quite different. 'Well, I guess I'll just have to introduce myself. I'm Mariko.'

She held out one delicate hand, and Andrea shook it rather awkwardly. 'Have you known E.J. . . . Edward long?' she enquired, struggling stiffly to make some kind of conversation.

'Oh, sure—he's been over loads of times to stay with my father. Though he's never mentioned you before . . .' The smile was sweet, but the eyes as sharp as knives.

'Oh, we . . . only met quite recently.' Andrea felt as if she was engaged in some subtle form of unarmed combat. Had that been E.J.'s intention, to pit the two of them against each other somehow? But why? It would serve him right if she were to blow apart the whole deception by telling this girl the truth right now.

But she wouldn't. Quite apart from the very real risk that he would take revenge by informing on her to the police, it gave her some small measure of satisfaction to know that she was causing the extremely self-possessed young lady opposite at least a little dis-

comfort. Not that she accounted herself much com-
petition for such a dainty, flower-like creature. That
was the sort his taste evidently ran to; like the blonde
she had seen him with in London—purely ornamental.

And it was ridiculous to identify her present turmoil
of emotions as jealousy. She was simply very tired,
and annoyed at the way he had sent her off into this
situation alone without priming her about what to
expect. She was getting a little fed up with his de-
viousness and manipulation—and when she saw him
again she would tell him so.

She drained her coffee, and stifled a yawn. 'I'm
sorry,' she apologised to her hostess. 'I really am *very*
tired. I think I'd like a lie down before dinner, if I
may?'

'Oh, my gosh, how mean of me!' Mariko sprang
gracefully to her feet. 'I never meant to keep you here
gossiping so late, after that awful long flight. But it's
so nice to have Western visitors—I just know we're
going to be real good friends!'

Andrea managed a thin smile, privately reserving
her doubts.

She felt uncomfortably conscious of her height
beside the tiny Japanese girl as she followed her
through the house—being with E.J. she had begun to
forget her awkwardness a little, but now it came back
twice as strongly. It was all very well for him to say
that a model would envy her—for an ordinary person,
towering so far above everyone around her, especially
with such a noticeably bright head of hair, it could
be excruciatingly embarrassing.

Though the house was all on one storey, it seemed
to ramble in a way that made her fear she would get

lost on her own. It enclosed several courtyards, laid out with the same simplicity and restraint as the garden. At last Mariko slid back a section of paper-screen wall, and announced, 'This is your bedroom.'

She found herself in another spare, tranquil room, similar to the sitting-room—there wasn't even a bed in it. Mariko laughed in superior amusement at her confusion. 'Oh, don't worry—Buena will unroll the futon for you while you are taking your bath. You'll find it real comfortable once you get used to it—and a whole lot healthier than a nasty sagging matress.'

'Thank you.' Andrea allowed a dry hint of sarcasm to creep into her voice—she was getting a little fed-up with being patronised by this arrogant little madam.

'The bathroom is at the end of the hall—you'll find everything you need there. Oh—you do know to wash yourself clean before getting into the tub, don't you? You may find the water a little hot, of course, but you'll soon get used to it. And don't worry about dinner—the men won't be home till past midnight, if at all. I'll have Buena bring you something to your room.'

Andrea absorbed this information with a trace of surprise. She had naturally assumed that E.J. would be joining her at some time during the evening—even though he had important business, he had no right to just abandon her. Oh, boy, when he finally *did* show up, was she going to give him a piece of her mind!

Left alone, she gazed around the room with interest. It was quite bare of furniture—there was just a large pot of chrysanthemums, beautifully arranged, in one corner. Her suitcase seemed to have disappeared, but a brief investigation led to her sliding back one of the paper-screen walls to find a spacious closet, where her clothes had already been carefully hung.

With some relief she stripped off the elegant suit she had worn to travel in, and slipped on a cool cotton kimono that was hanging on a hook just inside the closet, and, taking her toilet bag, went in search of the bathroom Mariko had pointed out.

It proved to be in a small wooden cabin just outside of the house, reached by a covered wooden bridge. The first thing that struck her was the heat—it was as hot as a sauna. The deep wooden tub was already filled, and she tested the water gingerly with her hand—and gasped in shock. It was scalding hot! She could never get into that.

Tears of foolish self-pity welled into her eyes. It was all so strange here—she didn't understand anything. And she had been so looking forward to letting her weary body relax in a nice warm bath—but now she couldn't. It was all E.J.'s fault—he could at least have had the decency to come to the house with her, instead of going gallivanting off heaven only knew where!

At least there was a shower, which wasn't too hot, though it was rather inconveniently set at about the height of her knees. Once she had washed off the dirt of the journey she felt a little restored, and, wrapping the kimono around herself again, went back to her room.

The bed had been laid out—on the floor. But Andrea was so tired that she felt as though she could have slept on the roof. There was a light meal waiting for her too, on a kind of wicker tray on legs. She sat down cross-legged on the bed, and drew the tray towards her, examining its contents with interest.

There was a delicious selection, set out in tiny laquered bowls—shreds of grilled chicken, sweet button mushrooms, smoked fish, vegetables both fresh and pickled, and little balls of rice flavoured with vinegar, salt and sugar. She wasn't particularly hungry—she had lost track of what time it would be in England, but her body hadn't yet caught up with the time-lag—but the food was pretty enough to tempt the weakest appetite, and she managed to finish most of it.

By then, the effects of the jet-lag had almost overwhelmed her, and she didn't feel as if she even had the energy to find her nightdress. Throwing off the kimono, she crawled naked beneath the covers, asleep before her head even touched the pillow.

That evocative male muskiness was filling her senses, reaching into her dreams. She came awake with a soft sigh of longing on her lips—and gasped in shock as she realised that she was no longer alone. E.J. was lying beside her, his head propped up on his elbow, watching her with cool amusement.

'What...? Go away! How dare you?' she protested breathlessly, realising with a flood of embarrassment that she was naked beneath the covers. 'What are you doing here?'

'I should have thought that was fairly obvious,' he responded, a lilt of lazy mockery in his voice.

'I'm not going to sleep with you!' she insisted, edging back away from him, hugging the coverlet defensively around her body.

'But you've been doing just that—for the past half-hour,' he teased. 'And very peacefully too. Did you know you have a very appealing way of snuffling in your sleep, like a little dormouse?'

Her cheeks flamed scarlet at the thought that he had been lying there watching her for all that time—when she had been dreaming such dreams! 'I...didn't mean that,' she protested, uncomfortably aware that through the translucent paper walls anyone could be listening to their conversation.

He lifted one dark eyebrow in sardonic enquiry. 'No? Then what *did* you mean?' he taunted softly.

'I...' She glared at him in angry resentment. He knew exactly what she meant—he was just playing games with her. 'This wasn't...part of our agreement,' she forced out.

'Oh, but it was,' he countered, those blue eyes glinting. 'You agreed to help me even up the balance in my negotiations with Tsutsumi.'

'Yes—by pretending to object to the building of your factory! I don't see what...*this* has to do with it.'

'It has everything to do with it.' In the darkness she could see that intriguingly sensuous mouth, curved into a rather chilling smile. 'You see, Mr Tsutsumi's a very clever man—he's more than capable of seeing through even the most subtle of strategies. But the principle of Akaido is to use your opponent's strength against him. So I propose to give him a whole web of strategies to disentangle. At the moment, he's trying to decide if I really have had the gall to bring my mistress along and pretend that she's something else—but then, he'll reason, I wouldn't make it so obvious that you *were* my mistress. So tomorrow, he'll arrange to have your credentials checked—and naturally, he'll find out that you really are who you say you are. Then he'll begin to wonder if maybe I'm sleeping with you to persuade you to drop your objections. You see, the permutations are endless. Hopefully, he'll still be busy trying to work out which are the false leads when we sign the contract.'

Her eyes sparked in cold fury. He had placed her in the most humiliating situation, casting her as the dupe who could be seduced by sex into betraying all her principles. 'What if I just tell him the truth?' she demanded belligerently.

He put out one hand to coil a finger into a long strand of her hair. 'It really wouldn't matter,' he responded, quite unperturbed. 'He'll simply think it's another strategy. You should have realised by now, Carrots, that it isn't that easy to outflank me—I pull all the strings.'

She stared up at him helplessly. His closeness was making her quiver inside, but she couldn't escape— he was holding her prisoner with his eyes as his hand stroked down over her bare shoulder. Though she had tried to deny it, this was what she had wanted, had let herself dream about—had let herself begin to hope he wanted too.

But that was before she had found out that they were to be staying in this house, and had met Mariko. Doubts and questions were swirling in her brain. What *was* his relationship with the pretty Japanese girl? Was he only here with her now because he couldn't risk going to Mariko in case her father found out?

His soft laughter mocked her confusion. 'If you don't want me to go on, all you have to do is say no,' he taunted, knowing full well that she would never summon the will-power to resist him. He waited for her to respond, and when she didn't he smiled in mocking satisfaction, trailing his fingertips down along her arm to loosen the compulsive grip of her hand on the coverlet.

A flood of shame washed through her as he brushed it down from her naked breasts. She was surrendering so easily, her protests only empty words. But her breasts were ripe and aching for his touch, the tender pink nipples pertly inviting, and as his hand stroked over her silken skin an odd little choked sob escaped her lips.

He laughed, a husky sound low in his throat. 'Why aren't you wearing one of those very expensive silk nightgowns I ordered for you?' he asked provocatively. 'An act of defiance? But I think I like you better like this—warm, and naked, and very, very desirable...'

Very gently he laid her back on the hard futon, and his head bent over the firm creamy swell of her breasts, his hot tongue circling one taut peak in a languorous swirl. She whimpered softly, moving beneath him in unconscious invitation, and he laughed again, mocking her surrender, as he caught the tender bud between his strong white teeth, nibbling at it lightly, electrifying her with a response that curled her spine, so that her body arched towards him as if to offer up the tender fruit for him to devour.

He lifted his head to look down at her, the heat of his gaze scalding her soft skin. 'You've been hiding yourself away in that laboratory of yours for far too long,' he taunted. 'It isn't good for you to let your life get so much out of balance.'

Was her need so blatantly obvious, then? She had to lower her lashes to veil her eyes, afraid that he could see too deeply into her soul. He bent his head over her other breast, and subjected that to the same exquisite torment, keeping the first rawly sensitised with his clever fingers, tugging and rolling the tender nipple, darting sparks of fire into her brain.

Through a mist of shadows she gazed down at him, shocked by the wanton thrill that shivered through her at the sight of his dark head against her pale skin, his moist tongue lapping at the hard pink bud of her nipple as if he were savouring the cherry atop an ice-cream sundae. And then as he drew it into his mouth, suckling it with a deep, hungry rhythm, she could think no more, her eyes closing as her head tipped back over the pillow and she lost herself in the world of erotic pleasure he was weaving so skilfully.

It was a prolonged torture, arousing every sensitised nerve-fibre to a shimmering tension, pulsing fever into her blood. But though she moaned and sobbed, her body racked with a hollow longing that could only be assuaged in one way, he neither stopped nor went further, holding her straining responses on a leash until she felt as if she was exploding within, torn apart by her own fierce hunger.

By the time he at last lifted his head again, her brain was scrambled and her bones had melted away. He laughed down into her dazed eyes. 'Well, Carrots, the question is, do we make the illusion into reality?'

She stared up at him, a hot flood of humiliation almost choking her. She had almost forgotten that he was only using her, that everything he did was coldly calculated to turn out to his own advantage. He wasn't making love to her because he felt any real desire for her—not her as a person, at least. Her presence in his bed was simply a convenient by-product of his machinations against Mr Tsutsumi. No doubt if Mariko would have served him better at this moment in time, she would be here now instead.

Angrily she pushed him away, kicking out at him and trying to hit him. 'No! Leave me alone! I hate you!'

He held her off easily, chuckling with laughter. 'All right—there's no need to go wild,' he taunted. 'Everyone in the house can hear you quite clearly enough.'

'Oh . . . !' She pulled away from him, so livid that if she'd had a gun she would have shot him. Even by losing her temper and shouting at him she had played by his script; she was beginning to feel like a puppet, manipulated by a master who could pull her strings whenever he wanted.

Smiling that infuriating smile, he slid back to his side of the bed and lay down. 'You'd better get some sleep,' he advised, a lilt of sardonic humour in his voice. 'It's probably the jet-lag that's affecting your temper.'

She stared at him in dumb disbelief. He was calmly going to go to sleep, right here beside her, as if it were the most normal thing in the world! And there was nothing she could do about it. She couldn't get out of bed, with no clothes on—her cotton kimono was out of reach on the other side of the bed. And besides, where could she go in this strange house, in the middle of the night?

And now her body really hurt, wound up like a spring and desperate for release, her breasts still aching from his touch, her nipples hot and raw. But she'd be damned if she let him know what havoc he had wreaked. 'Oh, rats to you!' she muttered fiercely, and turned her back on him, shifting over to the very edge of the futon, as far away from him as possible. If he could go to sleep, so could she.

She lay stiffly, quiveringly aware of the closeness of that hard male body just inches away, afraid to let herself relax in case she should accidentally move more towards his side—which he might take as an invitation she had no intention of offering.

But within a few moments she could hear his breathing, deep and regular. Angry indignation smouldered inside her—he was already asleep! And all she could do was lie here counting her grievances, instead of sheep. Easing her position slightly, she closed her eyes, and resolutely tried to forget that he was there.

But she couldn't do that; he was always going to be there, in her mind and in her heart, long after this nightmare week was over and she was back in England. She hated him, but she had fallen in love with him—hard. It was no good telling herself it was stupid—from the first moment she had met him, there wasn't a damned thing she could have done about it.

CHAPTER SEVEN

ANDREA awoke to find sunlight and shadows dancing on the paper screen that made up the outer wall of the room. For a moment she gazed at it in charmed fascination, and then memory came rushing back like a douse of cold water. She twisted quickly around. But the bed was empty. Only a slight crumpling of the white pillowcase, and a faint lingering muskiness, remained to taunt her with the confirmation that the events of last night hadn't been a dream.

A deep blush of scarlet coloured her cheeks as she remembered how she had crawled into bed naked, too sleepy to find her nightdress. If she had only guessed that E.J. was planning to climb in beside her! But how could she know what was going on in that devious mind? Once again he had manipulated the situation to his own advantage—and she had had no chance to ready her defences.

And where was he now? The sheets were cool—he must have been gone some time. Apparently he had simply got up and left without even bothering to say good morning to her. A stab of annoyance struck her. Wasn't she supposed to be part of some elaborate plot to do with his partnership with Mr Tsutsumi? So shouldn't she actually be *meeting* the man, instead of being left behind here, not knowing what she was supposed to do with herself? Or had the whole story been a pack of lies—an excuse just to get her here and into bed with him?

Impatiently she tossed aside the covers and rose to her feet. Mr E.J. Preston was in for a small surprise whenever he deigned to return from wherever he had gone, she vowed resolutely—he was going to find that the sleeping arrangements had been substantially altered!

At least the disorientation caused by the jet-lag had faded, and she was conscious of a small surge of excitement—she was really in Japan! The futon bed had been much more comfortable than she had anticipated, and, apart from that...unfortunate interruption in the middle of the night, she had slept well.

A brief exploration of the bedroom revealed, between the closet where her own clothes hung and another she discovered which held E.J.'s, a reassuringly familiar Western-style bathroom, clearly provided as a concession to guests. With a comfortable sigh, she stepped into the shower-cubicle, and let the needles of warm water splash down over her body, soaping herself thoroughly with a rather luxurious shower-gel she had treated herself to.

Why hadn't Mariko shown her this last night? It seemed a very petty piece of spite. A puzzled frown creased her brow as she rinsed the creamy white foam from her skin and stepped out of the shower, wrapping herself in one of the huge fluffy towels with which the bathroom was stocked.

This whole thing seemed to get more complicated with every turn—just when she thought she had figured it out a new twist was added. It would have been very flattering to think that E.J. had gone to all this trouble simply to seduce her, but she wasn't that vain. Besides, the explanation was far too simplistic.

No, she had been right last night—it had something to do with Mariko. But what? If it had been that she had been brought along as a kind of smokescreen for a pair of star-crossed lovers, Mariko would have had no need to be jealous; and, whatever she thought of E.J., she couldn't quite believe that he would so easily fall into one woman's bed when his desires lay with another.

Damn the man—it was a complete waste of time to try to work out his intentions and motives. He was a law unto himself, playing out his secret schemes and strategies. Well, from here on, he could count her out—she wasn't going to sleep with him, and she wasn't going to be a pawn in his devious games any longer.

She felt thoroughly refreshed as she chose a pair of cool blue linen trousers and a fresh white cotton shirt, cut on generously masculine-style lines, from her new wardrobe. She brushed out her hair, pleased to find that the new style had made it so much more manageable, and was inspired by the chic image she saw reflected in the long glass inside the closet to add a pair of chunky earrings of blue sea-washed glass, and matching necklace, from the collection of smart costume jewellery nestling in its luxurious suede case, slipping a bracelet of the same delicate-looking stuff over her slim wrist.

She wasn't at all sure that she was going to be able to find her way around the unfamiliar layout of the house, but as she turned a corner of the passage she found Mariko coming towards her. The Japanese girl had chosen to go for designer-chic today, in a pale cream linen suit that bore the unmistakable Parisian stamp of Chanel, and a neat little pillbox hat.

'Oh, hi!' Gimlet eyes surveyed the stylishly casual shirt and trousers, pricing them to the last penny; and Andrea, who had never cared much for fashion, felt a secret satisfaction at knowing that she would have no reason to blush for the quality of her clothes in the presence of this competitive little miss.

'Good morning,' she responded, injecting her voice with a hint of cool self-assurance she didn't particularly feel.

'I've been waiting for you,' Mariko announced brightly. 'I'm going shopping—would you like to come along? We can have lunch in town.'

Andrea hesitated. She could think of few thing she would enjoy less than spending a whole day tramping round the shops, particularly in Mariko's company. But the alternative appeared to be sitting around here, with no one for company, waiting to see if E.J. would deign to put in an appearance—and she had no intention of doing that.

'Fine,' she murmured with as much enthusiasm as she could muster for the sake of politeness.

'I'll tell Naoki to bring the car round.'

Andrea regarded the other girl with covert curiosity. On the surface she was all smiles this morning—but beneath it she could detect a hint of brittleness. Of course, Mariko would know where E.J. had slept last night—and she didn't like it one bit.

Completely to her surprise, Andrea realised that she was nurturing a private pleasure at the thought. It was an unusual position for her to be in—the love rival, the 'other woman'. And at the same time she realised that if she asked Mariko now to alter the sleeping arrangements she would lose all that.

Common sense told her not to be so stupid—but the thought of the girl's smugness if she knew she had the field all to herself was more than she could bear. Of course, she would have to bring up the subject eventually; but later, she prevaricated judiciously. When an opportunity arose to do it in a way that would maintain that edge of advantage.

It was a long drive into the capital, and Mariko whiled it away with aimless chatter about the wonders of the merchandise to be had in the shops; Andrea listened with half an ear, responding now and then as appropriate, but mostly lost in her own thoughts.

Why *had* E.J. brought her to Japan with him? If only she could read what was going on in that man's impenetrable mind as easily as he seemed able to read what was going on in hers! And why had he wanted to make love to her last night? Was it because he really *was* attracted to her, even a little—or was it simply because—like most men, it seemed—he could enjoy making love with any moderately acceptable woman who happened to be available?

And she had certainly been available—it shamed her to recall how much. Her only consolation was that it was probably always like that for him—she couldn't imagine that many women would be able to resist the hypnotic power of those laser-blue eyes. She would have been just another in a long line of conquests.

No wonder he had found it so easy to switch off, she reflected bitterly. It had been very much a take-it-or-leave-it kind of deal—he had made no attempt at all to overcome her qualms. Presumably he had decided that she simply wasn't worth the effort.

But she knew from past experience that simply giving in was no way to improve a hopeless situation. It was probably fortunate that things had gone no further last night—letting him make love to her would have been about as sensible as pouring petrol over a forest-fire, and standing back to watch the effect.

'We're nearly there!' Mariko's bubbling voice cut across her thoughts. 'This district is known as the Ginza. I'll have Naoki drop us off now, and meet us again this afternoon. It's real handy to have a chauffeur—parking in this town's worse than uptown Manhattan!'

Andrea could well imagine that it would be. The streets were a seething mass of people and cars, all moving purposefully and with discipline, but seemingly impenetrable. Tall buildings rose on each side, all glittering glass and colourful electronic advertisement hoardings, and fabulous shop-windows displaying a tempting array of stylish wares.

'Come on, quick!' She found herself being grasped around the wrist by a small hand, and dragged from the car as Naoki paused briefly at the kerb. 'We'll make a start here—apart from Macy's, this is the greatest department store in the whole world!'

It soon became apparent that shopping in Japan was a very serious business. Floor after floor offered a cornucopia to the dedicated consumer; it seemed you could purchase almost anything your heart might desire under the one roof—a whole floor given over to stationery and paper goods of every conceivable variety and hue, a floor of state-of-the-art cameras

and another of video recorders and televisions and
every kind of electronic gadget imaginable.

Andrea would have liked to linger among the computers, but Mariko was dismissive. 'Pooh—what do
you want to waste time here for? Come to the fourth
floor—I'll help you try on a kimono.'

It wasn't worth the argument, so Andrea went
along. And indeed it was rather fun to let herself be
dressed up in a swath of turquoise blue silk and satin,
tied with a broad sash, her feet in white socks and
silk sandals, her hair lifted from the nape of her neck
with an elaborate comb.

By the time all the fussing was finished, she was
laughing. 'Good lord—does it really take all this time
to get dressed?' she protested as Mariko made a final
adjustment to the pad in the back of the sash.

'Of course,' Mariko insisted. 'How do you like this
one? Will you buy it?'

'Oh...I'm not sure.' That was something that
hadn't even crossed her mind. 'How much is it?'

'This one? Oh, no more than four hundred
thousand yen.'

Andrea caught her breath in shock. She didn't need
to do any calculations in her head to know that that
was a very great deal of money. 'Oh, no.' She shook
her head regretfully. 'I couldn't possibly afford that.'

'But surely E.J. would buy it for you?' Mariko
queried, her eyes sly. 'He'd just love to see you in
this, I am sure. He really admires Japanese style. Why
don't you ask him for it, as a present?'

Andrea couldn't miss the sly look in the other girl's
eyes. She had come to the conclusion that Mariko
wasn't nearly as ingenuous as that flower-like beauty

could lead one to believe. 'If . . . E.J. wants to buy me a present, I'll let him choose it himself,' she temporised warily.

Mariko gave a tinkling laugh. 'OK. But if you're not going to buy this, you've just got to have those cute lacquered boxes you were admiring.'

'No.' Even in so small a thing, Andrea decided it was time to assert her independence. 'I think I'll buy myself one of those pretty paper fans.'

Mariko looked faintly appalled that she should restrict herself to such a cheap purchase; she was already laden with beautifully wrapped parcels. 'Oh . . . sure,' she murmured vaguely. 'They're nice.'

Mariko's enthusiasm for shopping appeared to be inexhaustible; the only respite was a long lunch at a glossy restaurant overlooking the busy street. Then there was more shopping, until the Japanese girl was side-tracked by the bright lights of a *pachinko* parlour.

Andrea was fascinated. The place was the size of a supermarket, row upon row of pin-ball machines like shiny clock-faces, and at each one a devoted acolyte sat mesmerised, pumping in the shiny steel balls that kept the monster fed. The noise was deafening, the temperature hot, and as a mind-numbingly tedious way of passing the time it seemed to be without equal.

But apparently Mariko was hooked; more so—though it had seemed impossible—than on shopping. 'Oh, you go on,' she responded with a distracted wave of her hand when Andrea reminded her that it was nearly the time they had arranged for Naoki to meet them. 'Make my apologies, if necessary.'

Andrea slanted her a searching look. She seemed totally absorbed in the game—but was it really the chance of winning one of the tacky prizes on display that was keeping her here? Or was it just an excuse—because she wanted to stay here in Tokyo for other reasons?

A stab of pure jealousy knifed her in the heart, like a physical pain. Was *that* it? That, unable to spend the night together under her father's roof, they had arranged to meet here in Tokyo instead—at one of the "love hotels" she had read about in her guide-book?

And what did that make last night? She felt as if there was a nasty taste in her mouth. To E.J. she had just been a convenient substitute after all, available and pathetically willing to satisfy his basic carnal urges. And all day she had been harbouring that stupid delusion that the lovely Mariko could be jealous of *her* when all along the Japanese girl must have been laughing at her.

She turned away, walking out of the noisy parlour as if she was in a trance, barely noticing the crowds that jostled her on the busy pavement. It must have been some kind of instinct that led her footsteps back to where they were to meet Naoki.

The sleek black limousine pulled smoothly into the kerb beside her, and the chauffeur jumped out to open the door, accepting her stumbling explanation that Mariko wasn't coming home without surprise—apparently it wasn't unexpected. As she gazed out of the window at the endless suburbs passing by, Andrea felt a single tear trickle down her cheek.

Andrea had endured a lot of sleepless nights recently, but this was the worst. She lay awake for hours, staring up at the shadowed wooden ceiling above her, memories of the previous night fuelling the aching longing that gnawed at her.

E.J. hadn't come home, and neither had Mariko. It had been an uncomfortable feeling, wandering around the strange empty house by herself, eating her dinner alone, served by the Filipina maid, who had seemed a little flustered, as if feeling Andrea's embarrassment at the awkwardness of the situation. Then she had tried to read for a while, but her book had proved too boring to hold her attention.

In the end she had gone for a walk through the gardens. Wandering along moss-clad paths and over rustic wooden bridges beneath the shade of cherry trees that were just coming into blossom, her spirit was soothed by the peaceful beauty of a scene that appeared to have been created purely by nature but which she knew must have been the result of the most careful thought. But the romantic poetry of the moonlight on the lotus-pool had tugged poignantly at her heart-strings, making her dream of 'if only's and 'might have been's.

At last she had retired to bed—the bed she had shared the night before with E.J. She really should have done something about that, of course—if she hadn't let herself get so caught up in that imagined rivalry with Mariko. Not that it mattered now, she told herself wryly. He was in Tokyo, with *her*.

Turning over, she tried thumping the pillow into a more comfortable shape. The irony of the precautions she had taken before coming to bed taunted her now—she had known he wouldn't come, so why

had she bothered? She was a fool to cry about it—
but the tears soaked her pillow.

E.J. didn't return all night. Andrea woke alone again
in the empty bed, the sight of the smooth pillow beside
her twisting her heart with pain and jealousy. Did they
think she was stupid, not to guess what was going on?
What would he do if she let out a hint to Mr Tsutsumi,
when she finally met him? What *could* he do? A small
chill ran through her. She had no idea what he could
do, but she could be quite certain that if she tried to
interfere with his plans he would take a ruthless
revenge.

But there was still no sign of the mysterious Mr
Tsutsumi either. The maid brought breakfast while
she was in the shower, and then she wandered at a
loose end again, exploring parts of the garden she
hadn't seen last night.

One discovery intrigued her; in a secluded spot,
sheltered from the house by a curving bank covered
in flowering shrubs, she found a kind of wooden pav-
ilion, with just a roof held up by four elaborately
carved corner-posts, and a raised wooden floor. She
couldn't imagine what it was used for—it didn't seem
to be a temple or anything like that.

She was just resolving to ask E.J. about it when
the sound of a footstep on the path behind her made
her turn swiftly. But it was Naoki, the chauffeur,
bowing with deep formality, evidently requesting her
to accompany him. Puzzled, and wishing she could
speak even a few words of the language, she
went along.

The black limousine was waiting at the gate, and with another formal bow he opened the rear door for her. '*A—arigato*,' she managed uncertainly, stepping inside. What now? Apparently E.J. had sent for her—at least that was all she could assume. Like a brown-paper parcel, to be left until called for, she reflected acidly. Just wait till she saw that man!

The drive took part of the same route towards Tokyo they had taken yesterday, skirting around the great modern harbour at Yokohama, where giant oil tankers and luxurious passenger liners from all over the world were docked. But then they turned to pass through a district of pleasant suburbs, not nearly as crowded or high-rise as Tokyo itself, with even some old-fashioned European-style houses and churches that must have been left over from before the war.

Finally they came to a modern industrial estate, very neatly laid out; it wasn't going to be very easy to find any complaints about industrial pollution here, Andrea reflected wryly—it all looked spotlessly clean. Naoki drew the car to a smooth halt outside a large complex of buildings, and came round to open the door for her. She managed another awkward '*Arigato*', gazing up at the sheer face of the building, all reflective glass that was about as revealing as E.J.'s eyes, wondering with a small tug of apprehension what was going to happen now.

It took quite a lot of nerve to walk up the shallow steps to the entrance—at least she assumed it was the entrance, since there were steps up to it, and a sculptural representation of some Japanese characters that could be the name of the company. But the glass was all the same, showing her only a bronze-tinged reverse image of the black limousine driving away.

But as she approached the glass slid silently away, and she found herself walking into a glass-walled atrium as high as the building, like something from a futuristic fantasy world. Steel girders and open walkways dominated the small figures in smart white overalls moving purposefully about—men and women wearing the same, each with a coloured identity-tag pinned to the left side of his or her chest.

Blinking in bemusement, she found herself addressed by a pleasant-looking young man—she recognised him as one of the grey suits who had met them at the airport, though now he was wearing the same crisp white uniform as everyone else. 'Dr Carter?' he greeted her, bowing with customary Japanese politeness. 'Most honoured. Please to come this way.'

He beckoned her to follow him, so she did; at least she could be reassured that she was in the right place, she reflected with some relief—she had been half afraid, when Naoki had driven off and left her, that she was going to find there had been some mistake, that he had dropped her at the wrong place, and she would find herself adrift like a castaway, unable to make herself understood, unable to find her way back to the Tsutsumis' house.

He ushered her into a lift, which rose swiftly to an upper floor. They stepped out into a carpeted corridor, lined with doors through which she could occasionally glimpse busy offices, stocked with all the latest high-tech equipment. There was an air of businesslike efficiency about the whole place; she was going to have to be very convincing in her role of environmental champion, she mused wryly—the people here would have every relevant fact at their fingertips.

Not that she was sure she was going to play the role; it would serve E.J. right, after everything that had happened, if she simply refused. Though he had probably predicted that she might, and would have some alternative strategy that would just turn it to his advantage whatever she did, she reflected acidly.

Her guide had turned down another corridor, and opened a door, ushering her into a small ante-room. She stepped inside, glancing around . . . and suddenly E.J. was there, his blue eyes glinting with mocking amusement as he caught her in mid-turn, drawing her hard against him and imprisoning her in his arms.

'Hi there, Carrots—have you missed me?' he taunted as she gasped in surprise. 'Excuse me, Koji,' he added, nodding a brief apology to her guide as his head bent over hers.

Her angry protest was smothered by his kiss. He had laced one hand in her hair, drawing her head back so that her body was curved against his with a devastating intimacy, and his other hand was resting over the neat curve of her *derrière* in a way that sent out quite unmistakable signals of ownership.

She tried to struggle, but with just a slight tensing of his muscles he warned her that she wasn't going to be allowed to escape just yet. His tongue was swirling languorously around the delicate membranes inside her lips in a flagrantly sensual exploration, and though she wanted more than anything to be able to resist him she hadn't a hope—he knew just how to melt her.

Her blood was heating to fever pitch, and she was helpless to control her responses. She was kissing him back, her arms lifting of their own volition to twine around his neck, her slender body pliant as he moulded her to him. All thought of where they were, of what had happened last night, had been driven from her mind—there was just this deep, aching hunger inside her, and there was room for nothing else . . .

And then through the swirling mists in her mind she heard another door open, and voices which stopped in abrupt surprise. Unhurriedly E.J. reached up and disentangled her hands from around him, his eyes glinting with sardonic satisfaction as he put her away from him. Flustered, she turned to find herself the subject of interest of half a dozen pairs of eyes.

'Oh . . .' She felt her cheeks flame scarlet, all too aware that her hair was tumbled and her lips crushed and bruised with kisses. Anger boiled inside her; once again E.J. had ruthlessly manipulated her, setting her up to play exactly the role he wanted her to play—his mistress, or at least the gullible fool he was duping with sex to silence her protests about his factory.

Laser-blue eyes met her fulminating glare with mocking amusement. 'You were keen to meet Mr Tsutsumi, I believe?' he remarked, as blandly as if nothing at all had happened. 'I'm sure he'll be able to answer all your questions.'

He turned to an older man at the centre of the group that had just entered, addressing him in fluent Japanese, and Andrea found herself being studied by a pair of very intelligent dark eyes. She returned the gaze levelly. She would guess the head of the Tsutsumi corporation to be about sixty; his greying hair was receding over his domed forehead, and his figure was slightly portly in the same immaculate white overalls that all his employees wore. But there was something in his grave bearing, and the deference of the other members of the party towards him, that identified him as a man of considerable importance.

'I'm afraid Mr Tsutsumi doesn't speak English,' E.J. explained quietly.

The older gentleman acknowledged her with a brief formal bow—if E.J. was unreadable, she reflected wryly, this man was completely opaque. Was he annoyed that E.J. had apparently brought his mistress along on such an important business trip, and had allowed himself to be caught with her in his arms in the middle of the office? Or had he guessed that it was all some kind of game—and if he had, what did he think of that?

And of course it just had to be that he didn't speak English! Whatever she wanted to say to him, she would have to rely on E.J. to translate. So much for informing him about his daughter's night out on the tiles with his prospective business partner! Once again, all the play was in E.J.'s court—why did she even bother to resent it?

The only thing she could do was try to maintain her dignity. So she responded to the bow with a polite smile, stumbling a little over the fragment of Japanese she had gleaned from her guide-book. '*Konnichi-wa*, *Tsutsumi-san*.' But it earned her a flicker of approval from those shrewd eyes, and another bow, this time accompanied by something like a smile.

'Well done,' murmured E.J. close to her ear. 'He likes you.'

She drew away from him stiffly, wishing she could find a way to set him at a loss, just once.

'We were just going to take a tour of the dye-stuffs production complex,' he added smoothly. 'I thought you might like to come along.'

'Thank you.' From beneath her lashes she slanted him a look that would have turned any other man to ice—but on him it had no effect. He merely returned her a smile of lazy mockery, and she had no choice but to suppress her impotent fury, or risk looking a complete fool.

'Did you enjoy your shopping trip yesterday?' he enquired innocuously as the party walked back along the corridor to the lifts.

She forced herself to bite back the impulse to throw him a boiling retort; if he was trying to goad her into revealing her hurt and jealousy, the best thing she could do was feign a total indifference. 'Yes, thank you,' she responded coolly. 'It was very pleasant.'

One dark eyebrow lifted a fraction of an inch. 'Really? I would have thought Mariko would have run you ragged. Let loose in a shop, with a credit card in her hot little hand, there's no holding her.'

She registered a faint surprise at the sardonic tone of his voice; he was apparently under no illusions about his light-of-love. But then he was the kind of man who preferred his women to be pretty little air-heads, she reflected acidly—like that bimbo he had had on his arm that first night she had met him. Or-namental and undemanding, merely a form of relaxation for the hard-working businessman at the end of a hard day.

'It was very interesting to see Tokyo,' she responded, her tone as bland as his.

'Of course. I dare say you'll want to fit in a little sightseeing while we're here—Naoki will take you anywhere you want to go. I'm afraid I'm likely to be too busy to come with you,' he added, a glint of mocking humour in his eyes. 'Though I rather had the impression that you wouldn't find my company particularly conducive to your pleasure anyway.'

The lift had arrived, and she chose to ignore his last remark as they crowded into it. Acutely conscious of the studied indifference of the executives around them, she held her head up, trying hard to maintain a façade of cool dignity. But forced to stand so close to E.J. as the lift doors closed, scenting the evocative male muskiness of his skin with every breath, she could feel her heart beating much faster than it should have.

'Although I shall certainly give myself the pleasure of taking you to see Mount Fuji,' he murmured, his voice taking on a low, husky timbre as he bent close to her ear. 'It's very beautiful—one of the most romantic spots on earth.'

She struggled to ignore him, knowing that he was deliberately tormenting her. The lift settled to a halt, and the doors opened for them to step out. She couldn't quite suppress the small sigh of relief as she let go her breath—and the amused watchfulness in Mr Tsutsumi's eyes, the brief, smiling glances exchanged between the members of the entourage, told her that it hadn't been missed.

Angry pride lifted her head. She had never experienced humiliation like this in her entire life. Her only consolation was that she was among strangers, whom after these few days she would never see again. And she would never see E.J. Preston again either—thank goodness. Falling in love with him was one affliction she was very determined to recover from!

CHAPTER EIGHT

As THE party moved off, Andrea found herself relegated to the rear, beside the young man who had been her guide before—apparently he had been briefed to take care of her. 'This area of production is controlled entirely by computer,' he explained earnestly as they followed the others through a swing door into a glass-walled control area, where white-coated technicians sat in undisturbed concentration before a bank of monitor screens.

'We are using the very latest technology here—it is usually completely unnecessary for any human being to enter the production area,' Koji went on, gesturing towards the vast maze of steel pipes and tanks below. 'The flow is constantly monitored by this equipment, and any adjustments can be made instantly...'

Andrea nodded politely, but she was attending with only half an ear to the solemn recital of facts and figures he was reeling off for her. She was watching E.J. walking ahead with Mr Tsutsumi, deep in conversation with him. It was clear that there was a mutual respect between the two men, and she guessed that it wasn't easy to win the respect of the elderly Japanese.

But gazing at those wide shoulders, moulded by an expensively tailored grey business suit that tended to emphasise rather than disguise the power of the hard male muscles beneath, all she could think about was the way he had held her in his arms, and the memory was making her heart beat a little faster than it should . . .

She was almost caught off guard as he turned to her suddenly, those cool blue eyes as always much too perceptive. 'I think this may have been one part of the process that was particularly worrying you, Andrea,' he remarked blandly. 'You were enquiring about the emission of toxins.'

'Oh . . . Yes . . .' It was a struggle to pull herself together quickly enough to answer, and she caught a sharp glint in Mr Tsutsumi's eyes. It was clear that he was seriously doubting her credentials as an environmental expert. She forced a confident smile. 'My main concern is about the level of toxins remaining in the solvents, and what happens to them,' she explained briskly. 'In particular the heavy metals such as cadmium.'

E.J. translated the question for Mr Tsutsumi, who nodded seriously—though Andrea noted that he glanced to one of his own entourage as if for confirmation that E.J. had conveyed her words correctly. Satisfied, he responded, though speaking to E.J. and not to her.

'Most of the residues are extracted and recycled,' E.J. related. 'There is very little chemical loss in the process.'

'Very little?' At least he wouldn't be able to accuse her of not playing her part. 'What are the figures, exactly?'

Mr Tsutsumi frowned impatiently, and issued an order to one of his minions.

'We will arrange for you to receive a full print-out of the information you require,' the young man at her side assured her gravely.

'Thank you. And what about the arrangements for storage and disposal? How safe are they?'

'You will have an opportunity to see for yourself,' E.J. stated, translating for Mr Tsutsumi again. 'We can include that in our tour of inspection.'

'*Arigato, Tsutsumi-san,*' she responded with a small bow, and was rewarded with a genuine smile, and a bow of marked respect. She felt a small glow of satisfaction—at least she had achieved something.

They moved on from the computers into a laboratory area, and she knew that in any other circumstances she would have been engrossed by all the latest state-of-the art technology in use. But with E.J. beside her, translating for her the explanations of what they were being shown, she found it impossible to concentrate.

Not that she could accuse him of doing anything to deliberately unsettle her, she conceded—in fact the manner he had adopted towards her now was quite impersonal. But her response to him was on a purely instinctive level, far beyond her power to rationalise or control. She could only do her best, listening intently and trying to ask the right sort of questions, and hope that no one would notice the way she avoided making eye contact with him, how careful she was not to brush too close to him as they moved from place to place.

Andrea had no opportunity to raise the issue of the sleeping arrangements with E.J. for the rest of the day—through lunch and through an interminable meeting of which she understood not a word. They were never out of earshot of Mr Tsutsumi and his entourage, and she knew for certain now that some at least of them understood English.

She managed to be patient, in the hope that she might get her chance in the car as they drove home, but she found rather to her surprise that they were to be accompanied not only by Mr Tsutsumi himself but also by the young man who had been her guide, Koji.

It was rather a strain to maintain a flow of small talk, but the young Japanese was extremely charming, keen to discuss with her the differences between London and Los Angeles, both of which he had visited several times. E.J. chose to take little part in the conversation, sitting back comfortably in the corner of the rear seat, but Andrea was aware of him watching her, those blue eyes as cool as ever. That piqued her, and she set out to charm the young man in return, surprising herself by almost flirting with him—something she had never thought she had any talent for.

At last the car drew up outside the house, but before the chauffeur could open the door Mariko had come dancing down through the garden. 'Ah, here you are at last! I've been waiting all day.'

Her greeting seemed to be all for Andrea, who could have been her oldest friend, but Andrea didn't miss the sly glance she slanted up at E.J. The other young man she ignored, and Andrea felt a little sorry for him—from the wistful look in his eyes, she would guess that he was badly smitten.

'Hurry and get ready—we have to be leaving soon,' Mariko urged, clasping Andrea's arm and leading her

up to the house. 'I'm just *dying* to see what you're
going to wear—you have such fabulous dresses.'

She turned to E.J., chattering away to him in
Japanese, as Andrea put together the realisation that
they were apparently to dine out this evening—it might
have been considerate of E.J. to have told her so. She
could also guess that Mariko had been looking
through her clothes. What had she made of all that
sensual silk underwear? she wondered with a touch
of grim humour. It would serve her right if it had
made her thoroughly jealous.

E.J. had responded to Mariko briefly in Japanese,
and then switched back to English. 'I'm sorry to have
deprived you of Andrea's company for the day,' he
remarked, the hint of sardonic humour in his voice
revealing that he was quite well aware of the undercurrents flowing around. 'I hope you haven't been too
bored?'

'Oh, I haven't been bored,' Mariko scolded him
archly. 'But poor Andrea—fancy dragging her round
that dreadful old factory all day. It's very naughty of
you.'

'On the contrary,' Andrea put in coolly. 'I was very
glad to have the opportunity to see it. After all, that's
why I came.'

Mariko allowed herself a look of frankly in-
credulous amusement, but then caught her father's
even gaze. 'Oh...sure,' she mumbled with a casual
shrug. 'You're into all that kind of stuff, aren't you?'

Her dismissive tone—as if it were just a hobby, like
stamp-collecting, and not the *real* business of a
woman—needled Andrea. E.J. detected the sharp glint
in her eyes, and laughed, letting his hand rest lightly

around her waist. 'Andrea has a doctorate in biochemistry.'

Both girls recognised the faint hint of mockery in his tone, but neither was sure which of them it was directed against. Andrea felt her jaw clench in anger. Now he was trying to play them off against each other. Well, she wasn't going to let herself be drawn into that. Tilting up her chin, she moved pointedly away from him.

'I gather we're going out this evening,' she said coolly. 'I'd better go and get dressed.'

She walked away, leaving Mariko to have E.J. to herself—an opportunity of which she would no doubt have been swift to take advantage, had not her father and the other young man been there. Glancing back discreetly over her shoulder as she slipped off her shoes in the porch, Andrea smiled to herself to witness the other girl's chagrin at being thwarted, as the men were apparently excusing themselves to go off somewhere for a discussion of their own.

Of course, it was ridiculous to think of it in terms of scoring points, she chided herself firmly as she walked to her room. She wasn't the sort to enter into that kind of competitiveness—and, even if she were, she would be hopelessly outclassed by the beautiful Japanese girl. But she really couldn't help it—she *did* feel a certain satisfaction at the memory of the look in Mariko's eyes when E.J. had put his arm around her, however casual a gesture it had been.

It took Andrea a long time to decide what to wear—she had no idea how formal the evening was going to be. In the end she settled for a two-piece in soft jade-green silk, with a little buttoned top, the skirt gathered

at her waist and swirling to a fashionable longer
length. In a sudden flash of inspiration, she used the
tie belt to wrap around her hair, holding it back from
her face, and clipped on a pair of bold gilt and enamel
earrings.

The woman facing her in the mirror was a stranger,
an elegant creature, poised and confident—someone
she would have envied if she had passed her in the
street. E.J. Preston's mistress? At least she looked the
part.

'May I come in?' Mariko didn't wait for an answer,
but at least Andrea had the satisfaction of seeing the
fleeting look of chagrin in her eyes. 'Oh... What a
lovely dress.' The words seemed almost to choke her.

Andrea returned her a cool smile. 'Thank you—
yours is very pretty, too.' The Japanese girl certainly
didn't intend to let anyone cast her into the shade;
her dress was a confection of fuchsia-pink ruffles that
would turn heads anywhere.

'Oh, do you think so?' Mariko fluttered in a show
of irritatingly self-deprecating modesty. 'It's just an
old thing...'

They both turned at the sound of a footfall in the
passage, and E.J. came into the room. 'Good
evening,' he greeted them, his smile passing from one
to the other. 'Ah, you're nearly ready—good. I just
popped in to change my shirt.'

With casual unconcern, he was already discarding
his jacket as he crossed the room. Andrea felt herself
go suddenly hot; he had pulled off his tie and was
unbuttoning his shirt, but she couldn't obey her instinct to escape—not with Mariko standing there
watching like a hawk for her every reaction.

'That's a nice outfit,' E.J. remarked, letting his approving gaze slide over Andrea's dress. 'Is it new?'

She shot him a fulminating glare. What was he playing at now? He knew full well it was new! His eyes glinted in devilish amusement, and he came towards her, his shirt open and loose to show the smattering of rough dark hair across his bronzed chest, the hard bands of muscle across his stomach.

'My favourite colour, too,' he murmured, catching her around the waist and drawing her against him. As she tensed in indignation, trying to draw back, he bent his head as if to nuzzle sensuously at her ear. 'And a great improvement on your mother's hideous sweaters,' he added in a mocking voice that only she would hear.

Caught in the web of confusion he was spinning around her, Andrea didn't know how to react. With only Mariko there to see them, why was he keeping up the act? Unless...was it possible she had been wrong about what was going on between them? Since she had met Mr Tsutsumi, she had begun to think it odd that he would object to a relationship between E.J. and his daughter—rather, it had seemed as though he would be pleased. Maybe...

But at that moment she caught a glimpse over E.J.'s shoulder of Mr Tsutsumi himself, watching through the open door, smiling in satisfaction at seeing his two guests behaving with such lover-like intimacy. Fool, she cursed herself bitterly, pushing E.J. away— that little performance had been for *his* benefit, not Mariko's.

E.J. laughed in lazy mockery. 'There's no need to be embarrassed,' he teased, knowing full well it wasn't embarrassment she was feeling. 'Nobody minds.'

Her cheeks had flamed scarlet. She would have dearly loved to slap his arrogant face, but she had a feeling she wouldn't be allowed to get away with it. Besides, he was still holding her around the waist, and the closeness of that lean, hard body, the evocative musky male scent of his skin was filling her mind, so that she couldn't even think straight.

Mr Tsutsumi chuckled, and said something in Japanese that made E.J. laugh. He let Andrea go, and strolled back to the closet, stripping off his shirt. She had to struggle to maintain some semblance of composure, trying not to watch the smoothly honed muscles in his wide back moving beneath his bronzed skin. He selected a clean one from the closet and shrugged into it.

'So—are we ready to go?' he enquired, knotting on his tie and picking up his jacket. 'I hope I haven't kept everybody waiting.'

The restaurant they were driven to was clearly very exclusive—Andrea thought at first it was a private house, the building was so similar to the Tsutsumis' home. They were bowed into a private room by an exquisitely made up young woman in a beautiful gold and white kimono, and took their places around the low table as hot napkins were passed around for them to wipe their hands.

Andrea found herself seated between E.J. and the young Japanese, Koji. She was slightly intrigued by his presence; it seemed as though he was one of the family, and yet the way he occasionally looked at

Mariko seemed to preclude the possibility that he could be her brother.

The truth emerged over the bowls of frothy green tea that had been served before the meal. Andrea had taken her first sip rather cautiously, but found to her surprise that though it was a little sharper in taste than English-style tea it was actually quite pleasant.

'Oh—it's very nice!' she exclaimed, turning puzzled eyes to Mariko.

The others glanced at them both questioningly, and the Japanese girl tittered with edgy laughter. 'I'm glad you like it,' she simpered. 'If I'd known, I'd have had it served to you instead of the coffee.'

Koji laughed. 'Oh, no—you would still have served coffee,' he teased her indulgently. 'Since we spent some time in California, my wife has developed a passion for all things American,' he added to Andrea. 'I think she would like me to buy a Cadillac, and wear a stetson hat.'

'No, I wouldn't,' Mariko countered with a sulk. 'Don't be ridiculous!'

This revelation startled Andrea, but she managed to disguise it, sipping her tea, though her thoughts were buzzing. So Mariko was married—why hadn't that possibility occured to her? It explained a great deal; of course it would be imperative for E.J. to cover up their affair. But why had it been necessary for him to pretend to *her* too? she wondered bitterly. Couldn't he have just told her the truth? Did he think she wouldn't have played her part so well?

From beneath her lashes, she watched the inter-actions around the table, trying to piece together exactly what was going on. E.J., of course, gave nothing away—she wouldn't have expected him to. Mr Tsutsumi, too, was hard to read, but just once she caught his eye, and sensed that he was weighing her up, trying to decide if she really was what she had been presented as being. As for Koji, he seemed quite well aware of his wife's particular interest in their guest, but he seemed to have decided to tolerate it, at least for the moment—perhaps wisely recognising that with such a headstrong young lady there was little else he could do.

The food was wonderful. The kimono-clad young lady, and several assistants, came in and out, lading the table with innumerable exquisite bowls containing all sorts of intriguing, colourful dishes, beautifully prepared and served with as much attention to their appearance as their taste.

Andrea found that she was expected to just help herself out of any of the bowls, and on E.J.'s recommendation began with some of the delicate strips of fish simmering in hot sake, picking them out carefully with her chopsticks. There was another kind of fish, too, cooked in a feather-light batter and garnished with slices of fresh ginger and lotus root. She was a little amused by the way her companions drank their soup, slurping it enthusiastically straight from the bowl, but she imitated them cautiously, finding that even the strips of seaweed and chrysanthemum leaves were delicious.

The meal ended with several bowls of lightly cooked rice, which more than compensated for the fact that the other food had been rather less than filling, and then as the waitresses came to remove the empty plates

Andrea was enchanted to find that they were to be
entertained by two extremely beautiful geishas.

Both were wearing richly coloured kimonos, and
delicate ornaments of silk flowers and tassels in their
hair. One had brought a musical instrument, a bit like
a zither-harp, and her delicate hands fluttered like
birds over the strings as the other gracefully prepared
tea.

It soon became apparent that Mariko did not appreciate losing centre-stage to the performers. 'Of
course, I'd never usually visit a place like this,' she
explained to Andrea, her tone stiff with distaste. 'It's
only because you're here.'

Her father slanted her a frowning look, and said
something to E.J., who translated for Andrea. 'Mr
Tsutsumi wishes you to know that these are most tal-
ented and refined ladies, not "pillow-geishas",' he
explained, only the secret glint in the depths of his
eyes betraying his amusement at conveying this
message.

'Oh...I see.' She could feel her cheeks flushing
slightly pink, but managed a smile at Mr Tsutsumi.
'Thank you.'

He smiled back, bowing, his own eyes twinkling,
and she began to suspect that, though he might not
speak English, he understood it a good deal better
than he had revealed. He said something else to E.J.,
who chuckled with laughter, and nodded. Andrea
glanced up at him enquiringly for the translation.

'He said that a man who is lucky enough to possess
such a charming mistress would not require the ser-
vices of a pillow-geisha anyway,' he told her, tongue
in cheek.

She almost choked.

'The Japanese believe that we have two souls,' E.J. continued smoothly. 'They regard it as equally essential to nourish the earthbound, sensual soul as the spiritual one. A very pragmatic viewpoint, when you come to think about it.'

'Yes, I . . . I suppose it is,' she managed unsteadily. No wonder Mr Tsutsumi had accepted her apparent relationship with E.J. without turning a hair, she reflected with a quirk of wry amusement—he probably regarded it as as natural as breathing that a man would wish to ensure that his sexual needs were taken care of, even when he was involved in an important business deal.

And what of E.J. himself? Did he think the same way? He seemed to have adopted quite a few aspects of Japanese culture—why not that one as well? If he couldn't be with the woman he wanted to make love to, would he just as easily make love to the woman he could be with?

Her thoughts went back to that first night, and the casual way he had climbed into bed with her, assuming with all his high-handed arrogance that she would succumb without a fight to his practised seduction. And she very nearly had, she acknowledged to her shame.

And tonight they would be sharing that bed again. She really should have done something about it—he was likely to take the mere fact that she hadn't as some kind of invitation. Was that what it was? If she was absolutely honest, wasn't it because she *wanted* to sleep with him that she had found herself excuses to say nothing?

The problem was, she reflected ruefully, it was going to be very difficult now to demand a change in the sleeping arrangements. It was going to appear as though she was only doing it out of pique that he hadn't come home last night.

He glanced down at her, those laser-blue eyes mockingly perceptive. 'Something wrong?' he enquired in a quiet voice.

'No—nothing,' she responded, struggling to control the slight tremor in her voice. 'Why should there be?'

'You're enjoying yourself?'

'Very much.'

'Good.'

His smile hinted that he knew the turmoil of her thoughts. Of course he couldn't, she told herself insistently—no one could read another person's mind like that. But she couldn't quite dispel the feeling; he was so cool and clever, manipulating everyone around him, pulling hidden strings to make them dance to his music. Even Mr Tsutsumi was no match for him.

It was after midnight when they arrived back at the Tsutsumis' house. The silvery moonlight had transformed the tranquil garden into an ethereal fairy-land, but Andrea was too tense to appreciate it. She had been rehearsing in her head a cool, dignified little speech, but now the moment was approaching she wasn't sure if her nerves were going to be steady enough to deliver it.

She managed to wish her hosts goodnight with an awkward '*Oyasumi nasai*', and stepped into the bedroom. The futon was laid out on the floor, like a mocking reproach. Her spine was shivering like needles of ice as she heard E.J. follow her into the room, and slide the paper screen shut behind them. He moved past her to the closet, slanting a sardonic glance back at her as he shrugged his jacket from his wide shoulders, and hung it up.

'So,' he murmured, softly mocking. 'Everything's all right, is it?'

'No, it is not!' Her eyes kindled as she turned to confront him. 'For a start, let me make it absolutely plain that I have no intention of sharing that bed with you tonight.'

He lifted one dark eyebrow in innocent surprise. 'Why not?' he enquired.

'Why not?' She was discovering that it was extremely difficult to have a quarrel with somebody when you had to keep your voice low for fear of being overheard through the translucent walls. 'Because I have no intention of being your...your pillow-geisha, that's why not. If you want one of those, you'd better go and see Mariko!'

He laughed, shaking his head. 'Oh, no—I don't think Mariko would make a very good pillow-geisha,' he returned provocatively. 'They are chosen very carefully for the sweetness of their temper, and I'm afraid that isn't one of Mariko's virtues. The only time she's sweet is when she's just bought something.'

'Really?' Her voice was heavily laced with sarcasm. 'You surprise me. I'd have thought she'd be as sweet as honey for you. Rather sweeter than to her husband, even.'

'Quite possibly,' he conceded, his eyes glinting. 'Is that what's upsetting you?'

'Upsetting me? No, of course not. I really couldn't give a damn whether you're having an affair with her or not.' She tilted her chin at a haughty angle. 'I just want you to understand that *I'm* not going to have an affair with you.'

His smile was provocative. 'So you've said. I must admit, though, that if that's your intention I'm a little surprised you haven't asked Mariko to give you another room.'

She could feel a hot blush rise to her cheeks. 'I . . .'

'Do you know what I think?' he murmured, moving slowly towards her. 'I think you don't know what you want.' He was holding her prisoner with that hypnotic blue gaze. 'I was rather hoping you'd have left your mother's notions of morality at home along with those dreadful sweaters she insists on knitting you.'

'It . . . it's got nothing to do with my mother,' she insisted, taking a faltering step backwards, struggling to retain her defences against the spells that low, husky voice was weaving. But her heart was pounding so hard that she was afraid she was going to faint. 'It's . . . just that I don't believe in casual sex.'

'Oh, nor do I,' he murmured, his voice taking on a husky timbre as he moved closer, until she had nowhere else to retreat. 'I don't believe sex should be casual at all. I believe it should be slow, and deep, and warm, and sensual. But that doesn't mean it has to come with a neat set of guarantees.'

His persuasive voice was heating her blood, and she had to struggle to return his level gaze. 'I don't agree,' she argued, shaking her head insistently. 'Without a proper commitment, how can it be anything other than casual?'

He quirked an enquiring eyebrow, leaning over to prop his hands against the wall on each side of her shoulders, effectively trapping her. 'Oh? What about your previous love-affairs, then? You told me you'd had at least one. Did they involve a proper commitment?'

A flood of shame coloured her cheeks a deep scarlet, and she turned her head away, knowing how easily her eyes would betray her. But he took her chin in his hand, turning her back to face him. 'Tell me about them,' he murmured compellingly.

'It...it was just the once,' she admitted in a strangled voice. 'He was...I met him at a party. It was just a couple of days after my twentieth birthday. I thought...I was beginning to wonder what all the fuss was about, and... He had a car. It was raining, and we drove out to this place beside the river...'

He laughed, gently teasing. 'You did it in a *car*?'

She lowered her lashes to veil the deep humiliation in her eyes. She hadn't wanted to tell him, but he always seemed able to twist her to his will. 'Yes,' she whispered.

'And there's been no one else since?'

'No.'

'I'm not surprised.' He slid his arms easily around her waist, drawing her against him. 'It can't have been very comfortable.'

That mocking response infuriated her, and she put up her hands as he bent his head to trail a seductive path of kisses around the delicate shell of her ear, pushing him away. 'No!' she insisted. 'I told you, I'm not going to sleep with you.'

'Why not?' he coaxed, refusing to let her go, his warm breath fanning her cheek as he dusted more of those butterfly kisses across her trembling eyelids. 'Are you afraid of getting pregnant? I can assure you, I have no more wish to run that risk than you do. But there are steps than can be taken to avoid such devastating consequences.'

His words, though she couldn't argue with their sense, struck her with a cold chill. 'I'm perfectly well aware of that,' she responded with icy dignity, ducking beneath his arms and moving out of reach. 'I've already taken the necessary precautions.'

He shouted with mocking laughter. 'Oh, have you?' he taunted, lowering his voice again quickly. 'It seems to me that, whatever you say, you came on this trip *hoping* I was going to make love to you.'

'No, I didn't!' Andrea was furious that once again she had let herself be trapped into an embarrassing betrayal. 'I was simply afraid that you would...manipulate me into it.'

'Oh, manipulate you?' He arched one dark eyebrow in mocking enquiry. 'I don't think I'd need to do that—I only have to touch you and you start to quiver inside. But far be it from me to be accused of persuading you into something you don't want to do,' he added coolly, turning away from her and strolling across to the closet. 'When you're ready to risk experiencing a little real life outside your laboratory, let me know. Until then, you may rest assured that I shan't attempt to touch you.'

She stood staring at him in startled surprise as he calmly began stripping off his clothes, her heartbeat still racing like a drum. How could he switch on and off so easily, leaving her feeling so raw and vulnerable? If only she had that level of control!

'I'm afraid I don't wear pyjamas,' he warned, slanting her a sardonic glance as he calmly put his hands to his belt and began to unbuckle it. 'But don't worry—you won't be in any danger.'

Her cheeks flaming scarlet, she fled to the privacy of the small *en-suite* bathroom. What on earth was she going to do now? Oh, she was quite sure she could rely on his promise that he wouldn't touch her—and, after all, wasn't that what she had wanted? But how could she endure another night beside him, so close, the warmth of his body reaching hers, the scent of his skin in every breath she took? She would go crazy.

But she had no alternative. She couldn't stay here in the bathroom all night, and she couldn't prowl around this quiet, unfamiliar house looking for somewhere else to hide. And there were still four days left of their stay! If only she could leave tomorrow. But it was impossible; she was six thousand miles from home—and E.J. had her return ticket.

She lingered for as long as she could, changing out of her clothes and brushing her hair with slow concentration. At last she decided that he should have had enough time to fall asleep, though she took the additional precaution of wrapping herself up tightly in the cotton kimono—those silk nightdresses were just too sheer and sensuous.

Creeping back to the door, she paused to listen, but the only sound was of deep, regular breathing. Cautiously she slid the panel open, and tiptoed across the room. E.J. was lying sprawled face down on the bed, the sheet just covering the lower half of his body. She stood for a moment, gazing at the long, deep cleft of his spine between the hard bands of muscle, wanting him so strongly it was like a physical ache.

But he could never be hers—it was foolish even to dream. Even in fairy-tales, the poor girl who captured a prince was always sweet and beautiful. With a small, wistful sigh she turned away, and crept round to her own side of the bed.

Fortunately the futon was wide, and being firmly supported by the floor there was no risk that they might accidentally roll together during the night. But her heart was in her throat as she slipped beneath the covers, and lay there stiffly, staring up at the ceiling, hoping that the sound of her heartbeat wouldn't be loud enough to wake him.

But he didn't move, and slowly she began to allow herself to relax. Gingerly she eased her position, turning on to her side, and closed her eyes, hoping that at least she might be able to sleep a little. She was just drifting on the fringes of dreams when she heard his voice, that note of sardonic mockery telling her that he had been awake all the time.

'Goodnight, Carrots. Sleep tight.'

CHAPTER NINE

THERE was certainly plenty to see around Kamakura. A delightful old town, set amid wooded hillsides overlooking the sea, it had a tranquil atmosphere that was a total contrast to the bustle of nearby Tokyo. Wandering alone along the narrow streets, or sipping green tea in the secluded gardens of an ancient Buddhist shrine, Andrea found a kind of balm to soothe her troubled spirit and give her the strength to cope with the pain that was gnawing at her heart.

E.J. had kept his promise to the letter. Each evening they had gone out with Mr Tsutsumi and his daughter and son-in-law—once to the Kabuki theatre, and once to the Sumo wrestling. In public, his behaviour had been charming—no one could have guessed that anything was amiss. But each night she had lain beside him on that futon on the floor, listening to the sound of his breathing, staring up at the ceiling until the pattern of the wood seemed to be engraved on her eyes.

After Mariko's remarks about the theatre, Andrea had been wondering what sort of evening she was in for when they went. But in fact she enjoyed herself enormously. The acting was nothing like that she was familiar with, and of course she couldn't understand a word of the dialogue, but it didn't seem to matter. The sheer spectacle of the superb costumes and elaborate masks, the hypnotic chanting of the group of

narrators at the side of the stage and the melodramatic, stylised gestures of the main characters wove
an atmosphere that caught at the emotions, tran-
scending all boundaries of language and culture.

The Sumo, too, was an experience she had been
unable to imagine. The hot anticipation of the crowd,
building to a fever pitch as the giant contestants strode
into the ring, awesome in their dignity, caught her up,
and though she found the complex of rules and ritual
bewildering she cheered as passionately as everyone
else as the titans finally clashed.

But by the third day of sightseeing, Andrea was becoming bored; how many temples and lotus pools and
statues of the Buddha did you really need to see? She
had done a little more shopping, much preferring the
quaint little shops around the quiet main street to the
huge department stores of the Ginza; a set of delicate
wind-chimes, like those hung around the temples, and
a beautifully lacquered jewellery box, painted red and
black, with lots of tiny, intricate drawers lined with
silk. It was a pity she couldn't take home some of the
brightly coloured Japanese sweets for her nieces and
nephews, she reflected wryly, but that was just one
of the consequences of the lies she had been forced
to tell.

The house seemed to be empty when Naoki brought
her home in the late afternoon. She left her purchases
in the closet in her room, and wandered out into the
garden again. The cherry blossom was at its most
perfect, each delicate flower flushed with soft pink,
its fragrance scenting the warm spring air.

And as she wandered further from the house than
she had been before, she recognised the muted sound

in the background as the sound of the sea; she hadn't realised that it was so close. Exploring down the winding paths, she turned a corner, and found herself to her delight in a sheltered cove, lapped by the shimmering blue waters of the Pacific Ocean.

Slipping off her sandals, she walked barefoot over the soft grey volcanic sand, down to the water's edge. A little way out there was a jumble of weirdly shaped black rocks, jutting up like sugar-loaves, and, sheltering her eyes with her hand from the bright glare of the sun sparkling on the dancing water, she could just make out the misty hills far away on the other side of the bay.

Sinking down into the sand, she tucked up her knees, watching a couple of white terns hovering gracefully over the gentle waves, occasionally plunging for a catch and swooping off with it, only to return a short while later. They must have chicks to feed somewhere—after all, it was spring, and all of nature was busy with the task of mating and breeding, and bringing up the next generation, following the most basic instinct of all.

A wistful little sigh escaped her lips. Sometimes she had wondered if she would ever get the chance to do the same—be like her sisters, have babies of her own. It hadn't seemed like too much to wish for—it wasn't as if she was asking for the pot of gold at the end of the rainbow...

'I see you found the beach.'

She turned sharply at the sound of that familiar voice. 'Oh... You made me jump—I didn't hear you coming,' she gasped breathlessly.

A smile flickered across those laser-blue eyes; he knew it was more than merely being startled that had shaken her. 'I came to look for you,' he said. 'Naoki said you'd come this way. Mr Tsutsumi has invited us to be his guests at a tea ceremony.'

'Oh... Thank you.' She glanced up at him enquiringly. 'How are your negotiations going? Have you signed the contract yet?'

'Almost.' There was a strange irony in his smile. 'After the tea ceremony, Koji has invited me to engage in a bout of Aikido. I believe we'll be signing the contract after that. Our host,' he added on an inflexion of wry humour, 'is a descendant of the ancient Shoguns who once ruled Japan, and he still prefers the old ways of settling matters.'

Andrea blinked in bewilderment. They were proposing to conclude an important business contract over a symbolic bout of martial combat? It seemed bizarre—and yet she had come to realise since she had been here how deep the old traditions were that lay beneath the veneer of twentieth-century modernity. And the Japanese had no intention of letting them go.

And what about Koji? It had seemed all along that he was taking his wife's infidelity a little too coolly. Was this his way of dealing with it? A small shiver ran down her spine. How good was he? He must be very good, if Mr Tsutsumi was prepared to gamble the contract on the outcome of the bout. And though E.J. was a first dan in England, Koji was Japanese— he had probably been learning the skills from his cradle.

She cast a covert glance up at the man by her side. He was smiling, apparently quite relaxed, but she sensed a vibrancy in him, something honed and waiting. She strongly suspected that he was going to enjoy the added edge of spice the undercurrents of tension were going to add to the fight. But she wasn't sure if she was going to enjoy watching it. What if he got hurt?

Andrea hadn't noticed the tea house before, tucked away in a secluded corner of the garden. It was reached by a narrow, winding path, crossed by a pebbled stream that gurgled and danced in the afternoon sunlight. Copying E.J., she slipped off her shoes at the door, and followed him into the quiet interior.

Mr Tsutsumi, who had changed from his usual tailored business suit into a flowing robe of dark grey silk, patterned in a lighter grey, bowed gravely to her as she entered, and beckoned her to sit beside him at the low table. Koji and Mariko were already there, and she sensed a sharp tension in the air. After days of manoeuvre and feint, everything was at last coming to its conclusion.

She was becoming used to the low, flat cushions now, and settled down as comfortably as the rest, accepting one of the moist little tea-cakes that Mr Tsutsumi offered her. It was hard to remember that this man was also the very powerful head of the mighty Tsutsumi Corporation, but he brought the same solemn dignity to the preparation of tea as he apparently did to the running of his business. All his movements were elegant and precise as he lit the miniature brass brazier beneath the tea kettle, and scooped the green powder into the caddy with a long, slender spoon.

The dainty porcelain bowls in which the tea was served were really exquisite, painted with a delicate design of chrysanthemums, each petal lovingly detailed. Andrea exclaimed over them in delight, and E.J. translated her words of admiration to their host, who bowed again, a smile in those serious dark eyes.

'You know, you've made a very good impression,' E.J. murmured to her softly. 'He likes you.'

She returned him a look of surprise. 'It didn't seem like that the other day, when I came out to the factory,' she whispered. 'He seemed to think I was a damned nuisance.'

'That didn't stop him appreciating your intelligence. He's still old-fashioned enough to find that intriguing in a woman. But then, of course, that's why I brought you.'

Her eyes flashed in angry indignation. 'Oh, really? I'm surprised you didn't plan it for me to sleep with *him*, then.'

Those cool blue eyes glinted with maddening amusement. 'Oh, I didn't think it was necessary to go that far,' he purred.

She turned her head away, burning with anger. He was mocking her, but she wouldn't put it past him, if he had thought it would be to his advantage, to sink even that low. He was totally ruthless when it came to getting what he wanted—and getting it on his own terms.

A small shiver ran through her as she thought of those nights she had lain beside him, tortured by the fierce longing that was raging inside her, knowing that he wouldn't touch her unless she was willing to sacrifice the last vestiges of her self-respect, and beg. And, to her shame, she knew just how close she was to doing just that—and there were still two nights to go.

She lowered her eyes, sipping the strong, frothy green brew in her bowl. The formality of the tea ceremony required polite conversation, but it was clearly something of an effort for some of the participants. Mariko had abandoned all care for appearances—her eyes were only for E.J., to the extent of almost ignoring her husband; nor could she bring herself to address more than the barest minimum to Andrea.

For Andrea herself, her emotions in turmoil, it was almost impossible to lift her eyes to E.J., or to manage more than a few mumbled words in response to his casual remarks. She found herself drawn instead into an alliance with Koji, chattering to him aimlessly about her sightseeing around Kamakura, and his last visit to London.

It seemed like hours that they sat around the table, sipping tea in that strained, formal atmosphere, before Mr Tsutsumi at last removed the tea-caddy and scoop to signal that the ceremony was over. Everyone rose to their feet, bowing to each other, and filed out into the late afternoon sunshine.

Mariko moved forward to walk with E.J., but quite suddenly her father stepped in, his face smiling but stern, drawing her to his side and keeping her there quite firmly. Her eyes betrayed her chagrin, but there was nothing she could do. He spoke to her quietly, and she translated for Andrea.

'My... father says we'll go on down to the *dojo* and wait for Koji and Edward.' Her voice was taut with resentment. 'He hopes you'll enjoy watching the contest.'

'Thank you... Er—*Arigato*, *Tsutsumi-san*,' she stammered, bowing awkwardly.

He smiled warmly, and offered her his other arm. Faintly surprised, she took it, and they walked down through the gardens, the two young women on either side of him; the elderly but proud head of his family and gracious host perfectly well aware of all the tensions bubbling beneath the surface, but determined that they would not be allowed to erupt and spoil the evening.

So this was what that strange building at the end of the garden was for, Andrea mused as she took her place beside Mr Tsutsumi in the *dojo*. Soft mats had been laid out on the raised wooden floor, and paper lanterns lit at each corner against the gathering dusk. Their warm orange glow added to the theatrical atmosphere.

The two combatants walked down from the house together, apparently in perfect friendship. E.J. was a good head taller than the other man, but she sensed that that might not necessarily be an advantage. Both were wearing the traditional robes of the Aikidoka—loose trousers of black cotton wrapped over by a white jacket—and both wore the black belt of the highest grade of master.

They stepped up into the *dojo*, bowing with formal dignity to the three spectators. Mr Tsutsumi responded with a serene nod; then they bowed to each other, and began a series of exercises to warm up, loosening the joints so that their bodies would be supple and strong.

'Watch them do roll-outs,' Mariko whispered—in her excitment the American intonation had almost vanished from her voice.

Koji was springing lightly on his bare feet; then, with a short run, he launched himself forward, diving over his extended arm into a smooth somersault, maintaining the momentum to bring himself back on to his feet in one movement. E.J. stood by, watching with respect, before performing the same feat himself, the two of them weaving across the floor space, sometimes leaping over each other's backs and landing from such a height that Andrea would wince, expecting them to hurt themselves.

It was almost like a ballet, fluid and graceful. She couldn't take her eyes from that tall, lithe figure, moving with supreme balance and power across the floor. This was the product of all that studied self-discipline, she reflected, a small shimmer of heat running through her: perfect physical control.

And then the preliminaries were over; the two men paused, neither of them even breathing heavily from their exertions. They bowed once again to the audience, and to each other, and then the combat began in earnest. Andrea caught her breath as she recognised from the glint in each pair of eyes as they circled around each other, weighing each other up, that all thought of friendship was forgotten. This was the real thing.

It was swift and exciting, an ebb and flow of move and counter-move, of patient waiting and swift evasion, precise balance and swirling tumbles; the two men were well-matched, and it was impossible to see who was winning. For the first time in their acquaintance, Mr Tsutsumi was becoming animated, urging the combatants on and applauding each skilful execution of technique. At one point he leaned across and spoke to Andrea, forgetting in his eagerness that she couldn't understand a word of what he was saying.

'My father says that Koji has met his match,' Mariko translated, her eyes glittering with open admiration. 'You see how he uses the principle of effective distance to blend with and redirect the attack? It is called "the way of harmony". Contrast this with the clash and noise of your Western boxing.'

Andrea nodded, not wanting to take her eyes off the bout for a second. Koji was moving in for another attack, but E.J. side-stepped sharply, grasping his wrist and ducking beneath his arm to twist it straight up behind his back. Koji rose on to his toes, gasping in pain, and slapped his thigh with his free hand.

At once E.J. released the hold, and they broke apart, bowing to each other again in genuine mutual respect. But it seemed that E.J. had scored the first point, and Andrea sensed a sudden increase in the intensity with which they watched each other as they circled around the floor, each waiting for the other to step into his sphere of defence.

She flickered a brief glance towards Mariko. The Japanese girl was kneeling up, her hands clasped, her every thought written plainly on her face. She seemed to have forgotten all thoughts of discretion. Her father seemed intent only on the two men, confronting each other in the strange, atavistic ritual combat, but he certainly wasn't unaware of what was going on. How could she be so silly and selfish? And how could E.J. be fool enough to let his attraction for a pretty face jeopardise all his careful planning over the past eighteen months?

He wouldn't, of course. The realisation struck her so forcefully that she almost gasped aloud. Certainly Mariko was very pretty—and had made it more than clear that she was crazy about him. But that didn't mean he would inevitably respond. Unlike Brian, for instance, who had so few opportunities he was inclined to take up the slightest encouragement from any reasonably presentable woman, E.J. could afford to be highly selective.

Her heartbeat had begun to race a little faster. Of course, even if she was right, it didn't necessarily improve her own position—he had brought her along as a shield against Mariko, instead of a blind for her father and husband, that was all. But she couldn't help feeling a little lighter, knowing that he had been more honest in her bed than she had given him credit for.

It was E.J. who closed the attack first this time, a sudden darting lunge that caught Koji out. But the smaller man was as quick, tumbling out of E.J.'s clasp and on to his feet again, and suddenly it was E.J. who was flying through the air. Koji spun, keeping his grip on E.J.'s wrist, so that his own momentum completed the twisting manoeuvre, and it was E.J. who was on his knees, his face rigid with pain as Koji ruthlessly applied the hold.

Both Andrea and Mariko were betrayed into a gasp of horror, and Mariko almost scrambled to her feet. But as E.J. slapped his thigh Koji let him go, and he rose, smiling as he flexed his wrist, his formal bow acknowledging the other man's expertise with respect, his eyes giving notice that no quarter would be expected or given.

When the end came, it was as unexpected to the audience as it was to the defeated—it was so swift that Andrea didn't even have time to see what had happened. One moment there was all swift movement, the two men twisting and ducking around each other in a bewildering spin of holds and throws, and then suddenly Koji was on his knees, his elbow and wrist locked in a straight hold behind his back, so that he had no choice but to submit.

Mariko sprang up, all caution thrown to the winds. With a cry of joy she hurled herself into E.J.'s arms, hugging him fiercely, her excitement spilling over into an emotional flood of Japanese.

There was a taut moment of shock, as her husband and her father rose to their feet. Andrea stood up too, hesitant and embarrassed. This would be the moment when she found out once and for all whether she had been right or wrong about E.J.—and suddenly she realised how very important it was to her to know.

E.J. glanced around at the circle of faces, and laughed with grim humour; and then, taking Mariko's shoulders in a firm grip, he put her gently away from him. '*Sumimasen,*' he murmured, taking a pace back and bowing to her with the most punctilious formality. And then he side-stepped neatly past her to take Andrea in his arms instead. 'Thank you for your kind congratulations,' he added to the stunned Japanese girl. 'I am sure you will wish to congratulate your husband as well.'

The last thing Koji appeared to want from his wife at that moment was congratulations. He snapped something at her, his tone intelligible to Andrea though his words were not. She spun round on him, and then her father, but realised with a sudden rush of colour to her cheeks that this time she had finally overstepped the mark. She turned to E.J., but he was still holding Andrea in the circle of his arms. Her face crumpled in tears, and she fled in the direction of the house; Koji lingered only to bow politely to his father-in-law's guests, and followed her.

Mr Tsutsumi sighed wryly. 'I must apologise for my daughter's intemperate behaviour,' he said in perfect English. 'However, I believe we have a contract to sign?'

'Well done.' Andrea flickered E.J. a shy look from beneath her lashes as he followed her into their bedroom and slid the door shut behind him. They had just dined with Mr Tsutsumi—neither Mariko nor Koji had appeared—and the contract had been signed with great ceremony. 'You've got everything you wanted.'

His slow smile heated her blood. 'Not quite every-thing,' he murmured softly.

She felt the colour rise to her cheeks, and looked away, her lashes veiling her eyes. 'I . . . I'd better go and . . . get ready for bed,' she stammered, and then blushed deeper as she realised the import of what she had said. Swiftly she escaped to the *en-suite* bathroom, closing the door behind her as she struggled to control her ragged breathing. There was no doubt in her heart.

Whatever the future might hold, tonight she would spend in E.J.'s arms.

She stripped off her clothes quickly, putting them away in the closet, and stepped into the shower, letting the warm splash of water relax the tension out of her bones. Then she scrubbed herself vigorously dry on one of the big fluffy towels, and stood for a moment, gazing at her own naked reflection in the big mirror above the vanity-unit.

Rather a good body, E.J. had said. She had never thought of herself that way; she had always considered herself rather too thin. But her breasts were firm and round, pertly tipped with pink, and her legs were long and slender. And after all, he was the expert; if he approved, who was she to contradict?

That thought gave her a little glow of confidence, and she smiled slightly as she brushed her hair, and selected from the closet one of the fabulous night-gowns he had bought for her. This one was probably her favourite—of oyster-coloured rippled silk, trimmed with a froth of matching lace across her breasts and around the hem. Putting it on, feeling the sensuous touch of it against her naked skin, seemed to wake the first stirrings of anticipation inside her, and her mouth was dry as she walked over to the door.

E.J. was sitting up in bed, leaning back against a pile of pillows, that broad, powerful chest bare. As she came hesitantly into the room those laser-blue eyes swept over her, seeming to see right through the wisp of silk to the naked curves beneath, searing like fire.

'So,' he murmured, a hint of taunting mockery in his voice. 'Do I take it that you've finally made up your mind what you want?'

She moved towards him, but paused at the foot of the bed, a small whisper of doubt still troubling her mind. 'The other night,' she began awkwardly, 'when you didn't come home. Where were you?'

He smiled wryly. 'I was at a nightclub with Tsutsumi and some of his senior executives—trying very hard to pretend I was enjoying myself while they drank far too much and regaled each other with rather—er— uninhibited versions of "My Way" on the karaoke. I'm afraid that's another Japanese business custom that's usually unavoidable. Since it was very late when we left, we spent the rest of the night in a hotel in Akasaka.'

'Oh . . .' The explanation sounded reasonable, but she searched his eyes, trying to find if he was telling the truth. 'Did you know that Mariko didn't come home that night either? I left her in a *pachinko* parlour in Tokyo.'

He lifted one dark eyebrow in shrewd enquiry. 'And you thought I'd arranged a secret assignation with her? No.' He shook his head, leaning forward to take her hand and draw her towards him. 'I wouldn't do that. Though I've never wished to try it for myself, I have a very great respect for the institution of marriage. And Koji is my friend. How could you possibly think I'd have an affair with his wife?'

She blushed, a tremulous smile of apology curving her soft lips. 'I'm sorry . . .'

'Besides,' he added, his voice taking on a husky timbre, 'it was you I wanted to make love to. Don't you know that's the main reason I brought you? There were other reasons, but I could have dealt with them in different ways. I just wanted to have you here in my bed, to find out if I could smooth those prickles and reach the warm, soft woman underneath . . .'

He tugged gently on her hand, and her legs seemed to melt beneath her so that she slid down into his arms. It hurt to know that he saw her as just another challenge to win, that he was as far as ever from making any sort of commitment. But as those mesmeric blue eyes burned into hers, she knew she could only surrender.

'You've made us waste an awful lot of time,' he murmured, a hint of teasing in his voice. 'You're going to have to make up for it tonight.'

A shimmer of heat ran through her at his warning, but the anticipation that had been building inside her for so long had reached fever pitch. His hot mouth trailed across her temples and her trembling eyelids, and down into the delicate shell of her ear, as his hand slid slowly down the quivering length of her spine to curve over the soft contour of her thighs beneath the smooth silk.

'I dare say this scrap of nothing was ludicrously expensive,' he remarked with a hint of dry humour, 'but it was certainly worth every penny. There's nothing quite so sensuous as the warmth of a woman's body through silk.'

She would have disagreed; to her, there was nothing more sensuous than the rough smattering of hair across a hard male chest. But as her head tipped back into the crook of his arm, and his mouth came down on hers, the only sound to escape her lips was a soft sigh.

His lips were warm and firm, coaxing and inciting her to respond, and she yielded without a fight, her lips parting beneath his to admit the deep, sensuous exploration of his tongue, searching out all the sweet, secret membranes within. Her slender body was curved across his lap, and his hand was caressing her as the subtle musky scent of his skin inveigled her senses with every ragged breath she took.

She was shamed by the wantonness of her own response, but she knew she had been wanting this from the first moment she had met him. The certainty that she was a fool, that tomorrow, or the next day, she was going to regret this, was not enough to reinforce her crumbled defences. Some time during that fateful week when he had been chained to the wall, that dangerous physical attraction she had felt at the beginning had turned to love. And the fact that he knew it, and was prepared to exploit her vulnerabilty without scruple, should have been warning enough.

But it wasn't. His hand was moving over the smooth plane of her midriff in slow, sensuous circles, and a tense knot of anticipation was growing inside her as she felt his palm slide smoothly up over the firm swell of her breast, moving over the slippery silk, as the tender pink bud of her nipple hardened to a taut, inviting peak.

The thin strap across her shoulder seemed to have slipped of its own accord, and with cool fingers he brushed the scrap of lace and silk aside to leave her breast bare, the creamy skin flushed with the exquisite erotic sensations as he trailed one tantalising fingertip in lazy circles over the rounded swell, until she was almost sobbing with ecstasy.

He laughed softly, mocking her wantonness, as his thumb rolled over the hot, sensitised bud of her nipple, arousing it into ripe responsiveness, plucking it lightly in a sweet torment of pleasure. 'Don't be in such haste,' he chided, dusting the lightest butterfly kisses around the trembling corner of her eyelids and down into the delicate shell of her ear. 'Take your time. Let every moment linger—enjoy it to the full. Feel the pleasure deep in every nerve-fibre.'

His words were soothingly hypnotic, and she lay back in the crook of his arm as his kisses seared down the long, vulnerable column of her throat, lingering deliciously in the sensitive hollows of her shoulders, finding the tiny, frantic pulse beneath her delicate skin.

This was everything her fevered imagination had longed for, and more; he knew exactly how to entice and arouse her, exactly how to fan the flames of desire to a smouldering, incandescent glow, sustaining her at that trembling pitch for what seemed like an eternity.

And then at last he bent his head, and she felt the hot rasp of his tongue replace his hand, swirling languorously as he tasted the sweetness of her skin, taking one hotly sensitive peak in his mouth, lapping it with his tongue, grazing it lightly with his teeth, suckling it with a deep, powerful rhythm, and her spine curved into a quivering arc as she whimpered in mindless ecstasy.

His mouth returned to claim hers again in a kiss so tender that it seemed to melt her in a languid tide of honeyed warmth. His hands were stroking down over her body, and she was aware that he was stroking the lace hem of her nightgown up from her ankles, but as he laid her back on the cool futon she yielded in a sweet feminine submissiveness, parting her thighs as he sought the most intimate caresses.

The touch of his fingers on the soft, secret folds of velvet was exquisite. She was trembling inside as he gently explored, and then as he found the tiny seed-pearl of sensitivity deep within a spark of pure pleasure pierced her brain, and she cried out.

'What is it you want?' he whispered, taunting her with her earlier indecision.

'You. I want you,' she begged brokenly.

'Show me,' he teased. 'Show me what you want.'

Guided by an instinct as old as Eve, she reached out for the hard thick shaft of his manhood. 'Please,' she whimpered, parting her legs wider and drawing him in to her. 'Please...'

He took her with one deep, powerful thrust, making her gasp in shock.

Anxiously he looked down at her. 'I'm sorry—I didn't mean to hurt you.'

She shook her head. 'Oh, no—it didn't hurt. It was wonderful!'

'Wonderful?' He laughed, tenderly stroking the hair back from her moist forehead. 'That was only the be-ginning. We have all night—and all of tomorrow, and all of the next night.' He began to move slowly inside her, grinding and thrusting, stretching her deliciously. 'After exercising all that self-control, lying beside you for the past three nights and not letting myself touch you, I have a *lot* of pent-up energy to release. Do you think you can handle it?'

'I... I'll try,' she gasped, beginning to move with him as the pleasure tautened inside her.

The night was long, and filled with magic. One flesh, they sought together the pinnacles of ecstasy, soaring to heights Andrea had never known; her body was like a living flame, molten, incandescent. Neither of them needed to rest; one caress led into another in an endless erotic dance, hands and mouths and bodies seeking every kind of touch, until dawn found them sleeping, tangled up in each other's arms, finally replete.

CHAPTER TEN

'GOOD morning, Carrots.'

Andrea opened her eyes to find E.J. already making love to her. They had slept for only a few hours, and her body ached deliciously, but she couldn't help but yield again to the driving thrust of his manhood deep inside her, moving with him as he led her to the highest peaks of pleasure yet again.

Afterwards he lay back on the pillows, laughing. 'What an incredible night! I think that must have been one of the most amazing experiences of my life.'

She peeped up at him shyly from beneath her lashes. 'Was it?'

'Yes.' He rolled up on one elbow to look down at her. Her silk nightgown had been discarded at some point during the night, and she was naked, her creamy skin marked with the evidence of his touch. 'It turned me on so much, lying there night after night with you so close—I was just about ready to explode.'

Her cheeks blushed softly pink. She felt much the same; but she would have liked him to say something that might indicate he really felt something for her—that it wasn't just a matter of physical gratification. But she knew that was more than she could ever hope for.

'You have two choices today,' he announced, a lilt of humour in his voice. 'You can stay here in bed and let me make love to you for the next twenty-four hours—or we can go and see the cherry trees on the slopes of Mount Fuji.'

She had been lying back languidly on the pillow, enjoying the lazy way he was trailing his fingertips over her naked body, but at his last suggestion she opened her eyes. 'Mount Fuji?' She had longed to see it.

His sensuous mouth curved into a smile of wry amusement. 'You'd rather do that?'

'Well...' It was a difficult decision. She might never get another chance to see the romantic mountain that was the symbol of Japan—but on the other hand...

'Mount Fuji it is,' he decided for her. 'After all, there's still tonight.' He leaned over and dropped a light, tantalising kiss on each rosebud nipple, and then slid easily out of bed and stood up. 'Come on—Naoki will have the car here in half an hour.'

So he had already made the arrangements—she might have known he was only teasing her. She scrambled up, darting nimbly past him into the bathroom. 'Bags I have the first shower, then,' she insisted breezily.

'You mean I can't share it with you?'

'Not if Naoki's waiting for us,' she returned smartly, closing the door. 'Besides, if we stay under it too long we might dissolve!'

Andrea's first glimpse of Mount Fuji was a little disappointing; it was heavily shrouded in mist. But the lake was beautiful, a tranquil mirror reflecting the pure blue sky. They took a boat and rowed out across the smooth water, and as the sun climbed to its zenith the mist slowly burned away, revealing the perfect symmetry of the snow-clad peak, so exquisitely beautiful that it seemed almost the work of an artist rather than nature.

'I think I must have died and gone to heaven,' sighed Andrea, lying back in the stern with her fingers trailing in the ice-cold water.

E.J. smiled. 'This place is sacred to the Shinto religion. One of the most beautiful sights in the world is the view from the summit at sunrise on a clear day.'

'You can climb up it?' she asked, surprised.

He nodded. 'But it's a heck of a climb. It takes about six hours, and at this time of year most of the station-huts are closed. Besides, if it's misty there's just nothing much to see.'

'Oh ... What a pity.'

'The best time to come back is about the beginning of July. You can start off the night before, and climb up as far as the eighth station, and then have a rest before finishing off up to the summit.'

She smiled wistfully. 'It would be nice. But I don't suppose I'll ever do it.'

He seemed as if he was going to respond, but then changed his mind. From her seat in the stern she watched him covertly beneath her lashes. He was wearing casual clothes today—jeans, and a sleeveless black T-shirt—and the hard muscles in his shoulders moved powerfully beneath his bronzed skin. It made her mouth dry and her heartbeat race to remember how she had spent the night in those strong arms, had felt the weight of his body on hers. The images were so vivid that she had to look away.

They had rowed in close to the shore, where the last of the cherry blossom was drifting down from the trees on the soft spring breeze. 'They're such beautiful flowers,' she sighed, scooping up a handful of the sodden petals from the water. 'It's so sad that they last such a short time.'

'But that's the essence of their beauty,' he countered. 'They represent the ultimate truth of life—that all things must pass.'

She turned to look at him, her grey eyes misted. 'You really believe that, don't you?' she protested bitterly. 'Don't you think that anything can be forever?'

'No.' There was a harsh edge to his voice. 'That's something I found out very early in life. My mother walked out when I was six years old, and after that there was a whole series of women in my father's life— sometimes it seemed like there was a revolving door. The papers used to present him as the middle-aged playboy, having a jolly good time playing the field, but it wasn't like that at all—every one of them was the real thing when she first came along. But pretty soon he'd find out that it was his money that they were after, and he'd be broken-hearted. Until the next time. The crazy thing was, he never seemed to learn his lesson—he was just an eternal optimist, I suppose. That's not a mistake I'll ever make.'

'You think I'm after your money?' she demanded, stung by the cynicism in his words.

He shrugged his wide shoulders in a dismissive gesture. 'I didn't say that. The point is simply that you can begin a relationship with all sorts of high expectations, and when they're not fulfilled you can be in for a big let-down. Of course there's a place in my life for women, and I'd certainly like to carry on seeing you after we get back to England. But don't expect me to make any sort of statement about how long it would last, because that's something no one can predict. And it certainly wouldn't be fair to bring children into a relationship that wouldn't last, would it?'

'No,' she retorted hotly. 'But you can at least begin from a hope that it *will* last. If you're telling me that you're not even willing to go that far, then thanks, but no, thanks. You can have back all the things you bought me...'

He shouted with laughter. 'What on earth would I do with a suitcase full of designer dresses?'

'Give them to the next poor idiot who applies to fill the "place in your life",' she threw back at him.

He had let the boat slide up on to the crisp grey sand of a tiny secluded cove amid the dark volcanic slopes and primeval forest that surrounded the lake, and shipped the oars. 'So what are you saying?' he enquired, a note of dry mockery in his voice. 'That if I won't swear undying love you and I are over?'

She could feel the sting of tears at the back of her eyes, but blinked them back; she certainly wasn't going to let him see her cry. 'If you choose to put it like that, yes,' she managed, struggling to maintain at least some scrap of dignity.

He laughed in cool derision. 'What a pity. It was fun while it lasted. How about one more kiss, just for old times' sake?' As he spoke he had slid forward, trapping her in the stern of the boat before she could move. 'Maybe I can even persuade you to change your mind,' he taunted softly.

She barely had time to put up her hands against the hard wall of his chest before he bent his head over hers, and she felt the warm brush of his mouth, enticing and insistent, on her lips. She had had every intention of pushing him away, but it was already too late; temptation engulfed her like a tidal wave, sweeping away all her power to resist.

Just one last kiss... There was a bitter-sweet poignancy about it that brought the tears to her eyes. The sensuous swirl of his tongue, deep into her mouth, possessing her, stirred a response of purely feminine submissiveness inside her, and as she felt him unfasten the tiny pearl buttons down the front of her silk shirt she could only surrender.

His hands were so skilful, and knew her so well. He had scooped the creamy swell of her breast out of the dainty lace cup of her bra, his thumb rolling over the tender nipple to harden it to a sweet sensitivity, and as his mouth broke from hers to dust featherlight kisses across her face and down the long slender curve of her throat her head tipped back into the crook of his arm, and a small sigh escaped her lips.

His dark head had bent over her breast, his tongue swirling and lapping at the taut pink peak, and his hand had slid to the hem of her skirt, stroking it back up over the slender length of her thighs. She knew his intent, and she knew she ought to be stopping him, but she had forgotten why; if it was just her pride, after what he had said... well, she could cry tomorrow—all she wanted now was just these few moments of bliss. And there was no one here to see them; they were almost completely sheltered within the rocky cove...

'Are you really telling me you don't want me to make love to you ever again?' he taunted huskily. 'You don't want me to kiss you, to suckle your ripe breasts like this, to touch you here?'

His fingertips had slipped inside the wispy lace of her briefs, and found the tiny seed-pearl within its velvet lining, caressing it with such magical expertise that she gasped, her spine curving with the intensity of the pleasure.

He laughed softly in triumph. 'You can't deny it, can you? You want me as much as I want you.'

It was true; how could she deny it? Her body was filled again with aching longing, and as he slipped off her dainty briefs she reached for him, drawing him down into her arms. The boat rocked for a moment, lifting slightly on the water, but neither of them noticed. The sky could have fallen in, or the snow-capped volcano above them erupted, and they wouldn't have noticed.

He took her with one hard thrust, and she arched beneath him, stretched and filled, moving to his slow, powerful rhythm. The boat was rocking gently, adrift on the water, watched only by a black-headed crane fishing in the shallows. All her senses were focused on the molten core of her body as the tingling heat began to spread, sizzling through her blood and burning her bones, the flames beating higher and hotter, until she cried out, clinging to him as she seemed to explode inside and fall down, down into a crucible of liquid gold.

It was a long time before either of them spoke, or moved. And slowly, as sanity returned, Andrea remembered why she should have stopped him. She hadn't been expecting that this would happen while they were out during the day, and so she hadn't taken any precautions. He could have made her pregnant.

But it was too late to worry about it now—it was done, and if fate chose to be that cruel when she had been so careful she would just have to live with the consequences. But that was even more reason why this affair had to end as soon as they touched down in England. It had been like a dream, but like a dream it couldn't survive the harsh breath of his cynicism. It was over.

The powerful open-topped red sports car was in the fast lane, overtaking everything in sight. The man at the wheel was grim-faced; faint lines were etched at the corners of his mouth, and his laser-blue eyes were ice-cold.

E.J. glanced down briefly at the speedometer, and smiled wryly to himself, easing his foot off the throttle a little, and dropping back into the centre lane. This car had been a crazy indulgence; a limited edition, it would have been more at home on the Formula One racing circuit, and it had cost enough to pay off a sizeable chunk of the Third World debt. Sometimes he wondered what on earth had possessed him to buy it.

But he had done a lot of things these past couple of months that had made him wonder if he was going slightly crazy. He had been driving past the railings around Green Park one weekend when a painting had caught his eye, and on an impulse he had had his chauffeur stop the car, and had bought it. It was a bright splash of colour, totally out of place on the walls of his coolly restrained rooms. Every time he looked at it he wondered what had possessed him to buy it.

He had found himself losing his temper, too, and shouting at people—he who had always been so controlled. Maybe he was working too hard; since signing that contract with Tsutsumi in Japan it had been full steam ahead on developing the joint project, and it had taken up a great deal of his time.

Maybe he owed himself a holiday—though that in itself was out of character, he acknowledged with a quirk of self-mocking amusement. Even sitting here letting his mind wander like this—he had just got back from a business trip to America, and there were probably a thousand and one things waiting for him to deal with.

Resolutely shaking off the strange mood, he reached out one hand for the key-pad of his car-phone, and called his answer-page. Through the speaker he heard the click of the tape-machine, and forced himself to focus on the string of messages that had been left on his private line in his absence, pausing between each to dictate a response into his Dictaphone, for his secretary to type.

Suddenly a voice that was elusively familiar snatched at his attention; slightly slurred, as if the speaker was more than a little drunk. The person didn't identify himself—he seemed to assume that E.J. would know who it was. Impatiently he flicked the tape back to the beginning to listen to it properly. Who the hell *was* it? The memory taunted at the fringes of his mind.

'I'm just ringing to let you know... In fact, in a way, I suppose I've got you to thank—not that I'm going to thank you.' There was an odd inflexion in the voice as well—as if its owner was trying to sound casual, but was actually gloating. E.J. frowned. That mousy-haired type, the earnest environmentalist . . . the leader of the gang that had kidnapped him. But what was he rambling on about?

'You see, you thought I was stupid, but I was just biding my time. I knew she'd come back to me in the end. Oh, she was dazzled by you, and all your money—even the ones that seem quite bright can be taken in by all that flash.'

E.J.'s eyes flashed ice-cold. How dared he talk about Carrots in that tone of voice? She might be the most aggravatingly contrary woman he had ever met, and it was a deliverance for which he had since been profoundly grateful that she had walked out on him at the airport as soon as they'd got back from that cursed trip to Japan, leaving him with just a suitcase full of useless women's clothes—but that creep wasn't worthy to even breathe her name.

'Anyway, I'm ringing to let you know we're getting married.'

Married?

'On Saturday. Two o'clock in the afternoon, if you want to know—at St Luke's church.' Yes, that was definitely gloating. 'We might even drink a toast to you at the reception—but on the other hand we might not. We're going to Edinburgh for our honeymoon. Not as exotic as Japan, I suppose, but there's a very interesting symposium we both want to attend. Well, *sayonara*, or whatever you say in these circumstances——'

E.J. switched off the machine with an abrupt flick. So she was marrying the creep, was she? Well, jolly good luck to her; she had wanted commitment—she was more likely to find it was a ball and chain around her neck. How *could* she? He would have credited her with far more taste...! Not that it was any of his business, of course...

He glanced at his watch. It was Saturday today, almost a quarter to one. A little more than an hour to go...

Damn! He swung the wheel, slipping through a gap in the traffic and causing a van driver behind to hoot indignantly. There was a junction coming up, and he shot up the slip-road and round the roundabout, back down on to the other carriageway. Whatever else happened, he wasn't going to let her marry that...freckle-faced, mousy-haired cretin—he had bad teeth, too.

Accelerating smoothly, he moved out into the fast lane, and put his foot down. St Luke's church...but where? The likelihood was that it would be either near the university, or her home town—if it was neither, he had a problem. Reaching for his car-phone again, he tapped the code-button for his secretary.

'Hilary? Sorry to call you up on a Saturday—I need a bit of help... Yes, the trip was fine, thank you—I think we'll be able to put together an excellent deal with the Detroit end. I just got in about half an hour ago—in fact I'm still on the motorway, so when you've got this, call me back on the car-phone. I need to know the exact location of a St Luke's church...'

Good old Hilary. If anyone could come up with the information he needed, she could—and not complain about being bothered on her day off, either. She didn't even show any sign of astonishment at the peculiar nature of his request; no hesitation, no unnecessary questions—a secretary in a million. It was time she had a rise.

And she didn't let him down. Barely twenty minutes later, as he cruised up the open lanes of the M40, the phone buzzed. There was no St Luke's church anywhere near the university, so that seemed to narrow the field. Hilary had located the other; she even had precise details of how to get there.

'Bless you, Hilly,' he approved, a lilt of joy in his voice; the fates, it seemed, were on his side—he just had time to make it.

'I hope you get there in time, sir.' That well-modulated voice betrayed not even a hint of curiosity.

'Don't you even want to know why I'm chasing off there like this?' he teased. 'Though, to be honest, I don't think I even know myself.' He laughed with self-mocking humour. 'You must think I've gone completely mad, the way I've been acting lately.'

'Well... I had noticed that you had become a little more... impulsive of late,' Hilary acknowledged, the temperance of her language conveying volumes. 'However, I have to admit, I quite like it. It's made you seem a lot more human.'

'Really?' He arched one dark eyebrow in surprise. 'I wonder if you're right...?'

The smooth V12 engine beneath the sleek bonnet of the powerful car swallowed up the miles with ease, but even so by the time he reached the exit from the motorway a glance at his watch told him he had barely eight minutes left. Smiling grimly, he kept his foot on the throttle, thankful that the roads were almost empty of traffic.

Hilary's directions were faultless—he barely even had to look for the road-signs. Left at the second roundabout, straight across at the traffic lights and down past the common... he could see the spire of a church in the distance when a sudden flash of blue light warned him a police car was on his tail.

Damn—he was only just a little above the speed-limit, but the car drew attention to itself so provoca-tively that they had been bound to chase him. But he didn't have time to stop and make his excuses now—there was the church, and there was a white Rolls-Royce outside, with wedding ribbons across its bonnet. But all the guests had gone inside; it was almost five past two.

He braked sharply into the kerb, and leapt out of the car as the police car screamed in behind him. But he didn't bother to wait. Muttering a last-minute prayer that he wasn't about to interrupt the wrong wedding, he raced up the gravel drive and in through the wide oak doors, two policemen on his heels.

'Dearly beloved, we are gathered together here in the sight of God, and in the face of this congregation, to join together this man and this woman...'

The vicar had a small piece of beech-leaf from the churchyard stuck to the toe of his shoe. Black shoes, well-polished—a holy ordinance, performed each morning with religious zeal? Andrea wondered ab-sently. Brian was wearing brown shoes—with a grey suit. Poor Brian—he never did have any taste.

He had hired the suit from the same place she had hired her wedding-dress. A hired dress, for a rushed wedding, taking place for all the wrong reasons. In those first few dreadful weeks after she had come back from Japan, and confirmed that she was pregnant, she had cared so little about what was happening that she had let Brian persuade her that the best solution was to marry him.

As all the preparations got under way, she had begun to realise that she had made a big mistake. But by then there seemed to be no way out. It seemed so unfair to let Brian down, when he had been so kind— how many other men would be willing to take on another man's child, not even knowing whose child it was? And besides, there were her parents; they would be horrified if she had announced her intention of having the baby on her own—they were still old-fashioned enough to believe that a wedding-ring made everything all right. She was trapped . . .

The sound of a scuffle at the back of the church turned a few heads, and the vicar glanced up reprovingly. ' . . . If either of you know any impediment——'

'Yes, *I* do, dammit!'

Andrea felt one light-headed moment of joy, and then a dreadful flood of guilt. She had been hoping so hard for some kind of intervention that she had almost made herself believe she had really heard it . . .

'Carrots, you can't . . . Dammit, will you let me go? Carrots, if you think I'm going to let you marry that creep . . .'

Oh, no—that was far too vividly real to be her imagination! She spun round, her face deathly pale as

E.J. came striding up the aisle, a couple of policemen trying to snatch at his arms. The little bridesmaids, startled, scampered out of the way, but her father stepped forward to defend her.

'Look, I don't know who you are——'

E.J. was perfectly in control of the situation. 'Mr Carter?' He held out his hand, all smooth charm, and her bemused father found himself shaking it. 'I'm delighted to meet you at last. I hope your health is a little better—Carrots has told me all about it. And Mrs Carter,' he added with a dazzling smile for that startled lady. 'I can't tell you how glad I am Carrots didn't let you knit her wedding-dress. Now, if you'll excuse me for interrupting, your daughter and I have something very important to talk about.'

Somehow Andrea had found her breath. 'How *dare* you?' she demanded furiously. 'This is my wedding...'

Those laser-blue eyes glinted down at her in mocking amusement—but there was something else in them too, something that made her heartbeat skip. 'Why else do you think I'm here? I'm sorry to have cut it so fine, but unfortunately I was in America when that pasty-faced cretin left his message on my answering machine. I've only just got back.'

'Left his message . . . ?' She turned, puzzled, to Brian, who, far from defending her, was trying to retreat behind her, as if afraid E.J. would finally take retribution for that week in the basement.

'I just . . . I wanted to tell him . . .'

E.J. laughed with biting sarcasm. 'Are you really telling me you'd rather marry *him* than me?' he demanded, gesturing with contempt towards her cowering bridegroom.

Andrea turned back to face him, her eyes wide with amazement. 'Marry you? You never even asked me!' she protested indignantly.

For a fleeting instant, E.J. looked as if he had been as startled by his own words as she was. But then his eyes lit with certainty. 'Well, I'm asking you now,' he asserted. 'In fact, I'm not even asking you—I'm telling you.'

Before she could even gasp in protest, he scooped her up in his arms. 'I'm very sorry about this,' he apologised politely, encompassing both the vicar and her parents. 'But if I know Carrots she'll stand here arguing all day. That's why I love her—she's the only person I've ever met who *does* argue with me!' He turned to the two policemen. 'I'm sorry—I know I was speeding, but I was in a bit of a hurry. Are you going to charge me?'

The two of them looked at each other, and then smiled wryly. 'Speeding? Can't say we noticed, sir. Just take it a little easier this time, eh?'

'Of course—thank you.' And he strode off down the aisle, his precious bundle, all tangled up in yards of white satin, in his arms.

Andrea kept her face mutinously averted. Her mind was in turmoil; she was outraged at his high-handed behaviour, furious that he had made her look such a fool in front of all her family and friends, indignant for the shock and distress he had caused her parents—not to mention Brian—and rigidly determined that she would not let him manipulate her again.

So why don't you make him put you down? a small voice in her head taunted. Tell him to go away, go on with the wedding—if Brian was willing to continue.

Because she wanted to know what he was going to do next, she excused herself weakly. And because being held in those strong arms, carried off as if she were a princess in some romantic fairy-tale, was undermining all her rational good sense.

She was a little startled by the sight of the bright red sports car in the kerb. A cluster of people had gathered outside—some wedding-watchers who had been there when she had arrived just a few minutes ago, others no doubt drawn by curiosity at the unexpected arrival of the police. E.J. dumped her without ceremony into the passenger seat of the car, without bothering to open the door, and walked round to step behind the wheel.

'Better put your seatbelt on,' he advised, leaning across her to pull the strap down, his eyes glinting with sardonic humour at the fulminating glare in hers.

She turned her head away, studying to fuel her anger as a defence against the temptation to let herself surrender to his dominating will. If only Brian hadn't been so stupid as to ring and tell him about the wedding! He might have known that E.J. Preston would never let another man bring up his child—he would want to be in control.

The engine purred into life, and E.J. pulled out smoothly into the traffic. Andrea slanted him a covert glance from beneath her lashes. When had he bought this car? She had been under the impression that he preferred a chauffeur-driven Rolls to driving himself—so that he need waste not a moment when he could be working. And a car like this, so... attention-grabbing! Had he had a brain-storm?

They turned on to the motorway, heading for London. The wind whipping across the open-topped car was lifting her lace wedding-veil and making it drift out behind her, and she fought to hold it down, all too conscious of the curious stares she was receiving—not even keeping her gaze fixed rigidly ahead, looking neither to left nor right, helped.

'Well,' remarked E.J. drily after a while, 'are you going to sulk all the way home?'

She slanted him an icy look, and turned away.

He laughed in mocking amusement. 'Go on, admit it—you're glad I rescued you from that porridge-faced lump of gristle. What on earth possessed you to even *think* of marrying him? And don't try telling me you were looking for a commitment—what's the good of a commitment if you don't even *like* the person?'

'I do like him,' she protested, though her words sounded hollow even to her own ears. 'At least, there's nothing wrong with him—he's got a kind heart, and he's very well-meaning.'

He shouted with scornful laughter.

'Yes, it's all very well for you to mock him,' she countered angrily. 'But those kind of qualities are important. And he'll make a very good father.'

'So would I.'

'You said you didn't want children,' she reminded him, an edge of bitterness in her voice.

'Well, I've changed my mind,' he asserted. 'I want children. As many as you like. Though maybe not just yet,' he added on reflection. 'I'd like to have you to myself for a little while first.'

An icy chill shivered through her. Was that what this was all about? She slanted him a searching look.

'What do you mean, not just yet?' she enquired carefully.

He shrugged his wide shoulders in a gesture of easy dismissal. 'I don't know. Maybe in a year or so. Do you object to waiting that long?'

'But what about *this* child?' she asked, her voice taut.

His reaction, however, took her by surprise. He stared at her in blank shock, and then abruptly pulled over on to the hard shoulder. '*What* did you say?' he demanded, his voice slightly choked.

'I said...what about this child?' she repeated unsteadily.

'You mean...you're pregnant *now*?'

'Of course I am.' She laughed tremulously. 'That was why... I suppose it was the coward's way, but... You didn't *know*?'

He shook his head, still looking as if he had been hit by a knock-out punch from Mike Tyson. 'But you said...you were taking precautions. That's why I didn't...'

'I was. But that day we went to the lake...I forgot— at least I never even thought of it.' She stared at him in confusion. 'I...I don't quite understand,' she stammered. 'If you didn't know about the baby, then why...why did you come after me?'

He laughed happily, reaching over to unfasten her seatbelt and draw her into his arms. 'Why? Because I suddenly realised why the whole world's seemed so crazy these past couple of months. It wasn't the world—it was me. I was crazy to let you go. Falling in love with you was the one thing in my life I couldn't control, and it scared the hell out of me, so I tried to pretend it wasn't happening. But you've got me shackled up far better than when you had me down in that basement. You won't ever let me go, will you?' he added raggedly.

'No...' She shook her head, still trying to make herself believe that this was really true. But the look of anxious pleading in his eyes convinced her. 'Oh, no, I promise,' she whispered, reaching up to wrap her arms around his neck. 'And ... the baby ...? You don't mind that it's going to be so soon?'

'*Mind*?' For answer, he bent his head, and kissed her with such a fierce intensity that there was no more room for doubt. Cars and lorries thundered by unheeded just inches away. Even when a police car pulled up behind them, and two police officers climbed resignedly out and walked towards them, neither of them noticed.

'Ahem. Excuse me, sir.'

Startled, E.J. lifted his head and looked up.

'I'm afraid you can't do that here, sir. This is a motorway.'

E.J. Preston, he who was always so ice-cool and aloof, beamed at the bemused officer as if he were his best friend. 'I'm sorry—but we're having a baby!'

The policeman glanced at Andrea in her white wedding-dress, lifting one eyebrow just a fraction of an inch. But he had worked this motorway for years, and he had seen it all. 'Really, sir?' he responded phlegmatically. 'Congratulations. However, you're only allowed to stop on the hard shoulder in the event of an emergency. I'm afraid you'll have to find a more suitable place to continue the honeymoon.'

FREE
GOLD PLATED BRACELET

Mills & Boon would like
give you something extr
special this Mother's
Day—a Gold Plated
Bracelet absolutely *FRE*
when you purchase a
'Happy Mother's Day'
pack.

The pack features 4 new
Romances by popular
authors—Victoria Gordo
Debbie Macomber, Joan
Neil and Anne Weale.

Mail-away offer —
see pack for details.
Offer closes 31.5.94

Available now   Price £7.20

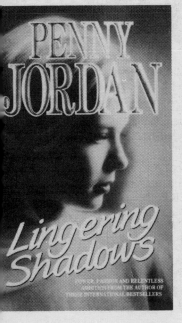

HEARTS OF FIRE

By Miranda Lee

HEARTS OF FIRE by Miranda Lee is a totally compelling six-part saga set in Australia's glamorous but cut-throat world of gem dealing.

Discover the passion, scandal, sin and finally the hope that exist between two fabulously rich families. You'll be hooked from the very first page as Gemma Smith fights for the secret of the priceless **Heart of Fire** black opal and fights for love too...

Each novel features a gripping romance in itself. And **SEDUCTION AND SACRIFICE,** the first title in this exciting series, is due for publication in April but you can order your FREE copy, worth £2.50, NOW! To receive your FREE book simply complete the coupon below and return it to:

**MILLS & BOON READER SERVICE, FREEPOST,
P.O. BOX 236, CROYDON CR9 9EL. TEL: 081-684 2141**

NO STAMP NEEDED

HOF

Ms/Mrs/Miss/Mr:

Address

Postcode

mps
MAILING
PREFERENCE
SERVICE